The Poets of Windhover Marsh

Christmas 2002

Dear Itoe,

I have been so excited to read
Pura, because he articulates
so much of what I find inadequate and shallow about North
American Christianity, and at
the same time creates characters
who are hungering for a more
authentic experience of God
through Jesus.

May these stories strengthen
and encourage your heart.

Love,
Suzanne

The Poets of Windhover Marsh

MURRAY ANDREW PURA

REGENT COLLEGE PUBLISHING
Vancouver, British Columbia

The Poets of Windhover Marsh

Copyright © 2001 Murray Andrew Pura

First edition

Published by Regent College Publishing
5800 University Blvd., Vancouver, B.C. Canada V6T 2E4
www.regentpublishing.com

Eletronic Page Composition: Greg Devitt
Cover illustration: Bill Pura

Printed in the United States of America

National Library of Canada Cataloguing in Publication Data

Pura, Murray, 1954-
  The poets of Windhover Marsh

  ISBN 1-55361-025-3 (Canada)
  ISBN 1-57383-205-7 (United States)

  I. Title.
PS8581.U65P6 2001   C813'.54   C2001-910428-6

DEDICATIONS

Five Loaves And Two Fishes is for The Peak Community Church in Denver, Colorado.

A Tourist In Moab is for Derek Rust.

Oregon Beaches is for Rod Peter.

St. Nate's-Among-The-Fools is for J.I. Packer.

The Poets of Windhover Marsh is for Eugene Peterson.

Last Night's Train For Lucknow is for the trainmen, J.I. Packer, Rob Clements, and my cousin, Greg McDonnell.

Daughter is for Micaela.

Good Night, John King is for Gerry Spence.

The entire volume is dedicated to Heartland Christian Community, where so much of what is good has become real (Micah 6:8).

THE WINDHOVER
To Christ our Lord

I caught this morning morning's minion, kingdom
    of daylight's dauphin, dapple-dawn-drawn Falcon, in his riding
 Of the rolling level underneath him steady air, and striding
High there, how he rung upon the rein of a wimpling wing
In his ecstasy! then off, off forth on swing,

 As a skate's heel sweeps smooth on a bow-bend: the hurl
    and gliding
 Rebuffed the big wind. My heart in hiding
Stirred for a bird, —the achieve of, the mastery of the thing!

Brute beauty and valour and act, oh, air, pride, plume, here
 Buckle! AND the fire that breaks from thee then, a billion
Times told lovelier, more dangerous, O my chevalier!

 No wonder of it: sheer plod makes plough down sillion
Shine, and blue-break embers, ah my dear,
 Fall, gall themselves, and gash gold-vermilion.

                —Gerald Manley Hopkins (1844-1889)

TABLE OF CONTENTS

CHAPTER 1

FIVE LOAVES AND TWO FISHES

His name was Bartholomew Scranton but to those who loved him he was simply Bart. Some well-wishers tried to call him Reverend but whenever this occurred he went glassy-eyed, so they dropped it. Others thought he might prefer the low-key designation of Pastor Bart. He grimaced at this also. It made him sound like a brandname product: new and improved Pastor Bart! Gentle and long-lasting relief. Pastor Bart with your meals. Pastor Bart at bedtime. Pastor Bart when you wake up. You can't beat Pastor Bart! People gave up calling him anything but plain old Bart.

He was senior minister of a church of 2500, working alongside eleven other pastors. Bart seemed to enjoy his calling. The other pastors knew better. "Big churches are a big headache," he told one. "Once you have more than fifty people it gets political," he told another. "Why can't we have sixty churches of twenty-five people instead of this Tower of Babel?" he groaned to his wife one night after supper. His daughter's nerf ball flew in from the hallway and hit him on the head.

One summer an aunt died that Bart scarcely knew and couldn't remember if he liked much. He got on a plane and went to her funeral anyway, was glad to see some of the family he hadn't seen in years, then returned home. He didn't think anymore about it until a law firm called. The aunt's will was going to make Bart a very rich man.

Bart had always said that you ought to enjoy your job so much that even if you inherited a million dollars you would keep on working at what God had given you to do regardless. But a week after three million dollars was deposited in their account, Bart rolled over in bed and said to his wife, "A million for the kids, a million for you, a million for me. What do you want to do with your million?"

Ruth had always had a soft spot for South America and for homeless children: "I'd like to give at least half to the missionaries trying to get food and shelter and the love of God to the street kids in Bogota and Rio. What about you?"

"I'd like to move to Denver, buy a small bakery, and have a church in our house. It has to be a house that couldn't hold more than fifty people."

Ruth laughed. "A baker? Since when did you want to become a baker?"

"I've always liked the smell of warm bread fresh out of the oven."

Ruth buried her head back into her pillow. "Just remember what happened to the baker with the dreams that Joseph met in prison."

Over the next few months Bart resigned from his church, Ruth organised a massive garage sale, and one morning they climbed into their Suburban and drove from San Diego to Denver. Somewhere off the beaten track, Bart found an old but sturdy brick building in which a German-American family had run a bakery for a hundred years before the grandchildren all decided to become bankers. He bought it outright from an elderly gentleman named Herman, who had been baking there for forty years, and then paid him a generous dividend to stay on for one more year to teach Bart how to bake all the European breads.

"How old are you?" asked Herman.

"Forty-two," replied Bart.

"What were you doing before?"

"I was a minister."

"And now you are going to bake bread? Do you know you have to be at work at three o'clock in the morning?"

"Well," responded Bart, "I used to get up at six to pray sometimes."

The old man laughed. "You will be praying over your bread."

The bakery had a dwindling but loyal clientele. Bart was content to keep it that way, baking seven or eight different loaves and pastries and stopping at 200 loaves a day, no matter which European-style restaurant demanded more. He would come home at ten in the morning, begin to dig into all the books he had never read, and fall asleep until lunch, which he and Ruth ate together. The afternoon was for golf or a hike, supper was with the kids, then he was in bed at eight, up at two. Once his body adjusted, he loved getting up early in the morning. The stars were like dew, the air was clear and cool, the fire and heat of the ovens made him feel he was at some wonderful spiritual task, as if he were a high priest offering sacrifices at the Temple in Jerusalem back in the days of David and Solomon. Prayer came easily and his spirit was more content than it had been in years.

Bart didn't bake on the weekends and every Saturday night a group met in his home. They sang to God, prayed, read the Bible, became close friends. "Don't tell anyone else about us," Bart always joked. After a year, there were twenty of them.

He said goodbye to Herman. The sign in the window still called it The Rhine Bakery.

"Thank you for staying on and teaching me the ropes," said Bart. "No more three o'clock in the morning for you now."

"I will actually miss it. Now I know I am an old man. I will stay in bed until six."

They smiled at each other, standing in the doorway of the bakery.

"Will you rename the bakery?" asked Herman.

"Yes. Bethlehem. It means house of bread."

"I am trying to understand you. What kind of man leaves a church to bake 200 loaves of bread a day?"

"A man who likes to get up at two in the morning and look at the stars."

Bart did not think he would see Herman again. But a month later he came to the door on Saturday night and joined their group.

"How did you know about us?" asked Bart.

"Your wife Ruth told me you met here for church."

That night Ruth could not get to sleep.

"Bart. Are you happy with the way the church is going?"

Bart did not open his eyes. "The church? The little group? Just the right size."

"Denver is growing, Bart. There's people coming to live here from all over the world."

"They're probably Bronco fans."

"How do you think God sees them?"

"What do you mean?"

"I used to look at the street kids in South America and think they were hurting and alone. Now I look at all the people on our streets, all of them trying to find a place to fit in, a neighbourhood to call home, someplace in this crazy world where they can feel safe. They're all street kids, Bart. They all need Christ, not just the boys and girls in Bogota. Is twenty enough people to have in our church? Just twenty? Is that all we're going to try and help?"

"Jesus had twelve."

"A year after the resurrection were there only twelve?"

"Ruth. That was then. It's two thousand years later. Church is too political. Too many people have had bad church experiences. It was easier then. It was fresh."

"Twelve hundred years had already gone by when Francis of Assisi thought he could still make a difference."

"All I want to do is bake bread. If God wants to build a bigger church in our house then he can multiply the loaves."

An older married couple, Eleanor and Benjamin, worked the store from ten until six. A driver began delivering the fresh bread at seven in the morning. Bart stood behind the counter from eight o'clock until Eleanor and Benjamin arrived, about two hours. It could be busy or quiet for him. There was no rhyme or reason. It was the part of the job he disliked the most. Maybe, he thought, I am tired of people.

Their second Easter in Denver rolled around. Bart looked at the batches of dough with his new assistant, Arnie. "You know," he said, "I'm tired of the same old dough. You've heard of paska, right?"

Arnie, who was a skinny kid about nineteen, shrugged. "Yeah, that sweet Easter bread."

"What about if we made fifty but with different crusts? I could make crosses in the dough. Or crowns of thorns. I don't mean drawings. More like sculptings, three dimensional, the whole loaf a work of art."

Arnie looked at the dough. "Yeah. Sure. Whatever. You think anybody'd buy it?"

Easter was a watercolour of greys and whites and blacks, smudging and blurring and washing over each other. It carried with it the soft gleam of pewter and, toward evenings, the dark shining of wet granite. Bart baked fifty loaves of paska for Maundy Thursday but the loaves did not sell. He gave them to an emergency shelter in the city's core named Jacob's Ladder. Most of Good Friday he slept, the clouds closing in around the city. Early Saturday morning he came to the bakery in a roaring, foaming rain that bubbled in the streets and gutters. The heat of the ovens dried him. Soon he began to sweat, his skin glittering with stars. He had given Arnie the Easter weekend off so he worked alone. He baked another fifty loaves of paska along with his usual breads. But the delivery truck returned with the bulk of them and no one bought any from Bart or

Eleanor or Benjamin. The Saturday group at the house was small, seven people, and everything, the worship, the prayer, the reading of the Scriptures, seemed lashed down tightly and restrained.

"Did the small numbers bother you?" asked Ruth as they lay in bed.

"No."

"Then what is bothering you?"

"I've made loaves of crosses and of thorns and even of his stripes. But people prefer the plain bread."

"What do you want them to want?"

"More than the ordinary."

"How many loaves did you want to sell?"

"As many as I could."

"Why? Numbers mean nothing to you."

"But if it meant they really wanted the bread. If it meant the thorns said something to them."

"What if there were 700 instead of seven next Saturday night? Or seven thousand?"

"I'm not going to draw parallels to that."

"But what if they were coming because they were desperate? What if the way we did church made all the difference in the world to them?"

"It won't work, Ruth. Once you get numbers it destroys something. Connections break down. Even if you use small groups during the week."

"Not if you did Sundays differently. Or Saturdays. Or Fridays. I don't care. It's how you talk, what you encourage, the kind of worship that's offered, that's what keeps the lines open. Then this fragile something doesn't have to be crushed. Bart, if you were able to take in seven of those street kids, you'd do it. Remember Angelica and Roberta and Dominique?"

"Yes, we'd take them in."

"Would you find room for another seven? What about Miguel? Miriam? Lucia? How many groups of seven would you take in?"

"Seven times seventy. But we'd need to buy an acreage."

"Why can't you open your doors to the orphans of Denver?"

"Because to you that means everybody."

"You'd open your doors to every orphan in Bogota."

"That's different."

"No, it's not, Bart. A million people alienated. No God. No home. No love. I don't care what they think they've got, money and sports and a good job, those things don't get deep into your soul when you're alone and afraid of the dark. Even the best friends and the closest family can only go so far with you. God knows we've been through the valleys and chasms where even our mothers and fathers don't know what to say. You see the cold distances between the stars. You see your mortality. You are absolutely alone. No yellow brick road. No lit up windows in the night. No doorways flooded with warmth and faces of good will. Nothing on the table. No towels on the bed. Every door is locked and even if you break in, every room is empty."

Bart woke at two, his heart rattling with a galloping, thundering dream, his mind raising him to get to the ovens. But he was not baking. It was Sunday. He lay and listened to the thumping of rain. Crows swirled among all his images. The grave was in a garden. A garden of roses and the spicy scent of pink and white herbs. What if it had rained the night before? The aromas would be even stronger. The birds would erupt into song in that grey hour before dawn. Didn't the women come just as colour was returning? Like blood returning to pinched skin? Mary of Magdala thought he was weeding. Just the two of them. Though another time 500 saw him. Crows swarmed and shrieked, a bastard file rasping at iron. He got up and dressed and went to the den where they had a small office. A fax sheet lay in the machine. Bart went to the kitchen without reading it, brewed some coffee, then returned. The red numbers of the digital clock on the coffee maker were 3:33.

It was their missionary friend in Bogota. The words were rushed. "Police have raided our orphanage in the jungle. On the streets, it is off-duty policemen who form the backbone of the death squads that hunt the children down. So, naturally, the boys and girls were terrified. Miguel and Francesco ran into the jungle and through the dense stands of bamboo where the motorcycles could not follow them. The other children were thrown into large blue vans, kicking and shrieking. The police say the orphanage has no license. On the streets they call the children garbage. Suddenly, when they are safe, the police must rescue them. We do not know where they have been taken. Our worst fear is that they will drive some of them to a field, open the van, tell them to run and shoot them in the back as their little legs try to carry them across the grass and stubble.

"Bart, I wish I had found foster parents for all of them in America. I wish they were in New Hampshire or in Minnesota or in Vermont. Or

Denver. I wish I had sent you a thousand."

Bart knew all the faces. He saw the two little girls with long black hair he had piggy-backed up from the jungle orphanage into town to buy them ice cream. He remembered the stench when he had opened the orphanage fridge: Large rotting soup bones, two bins of blackening lettuce. The children were eating soup for lunch, bowls of warm brown water. Hadn't he tried to buy them some fresh meat and fruit? They had stood in neat, clean shirts and dresses and sung to them in Spanish, all about the Holy Spirit and Jesus the Saving One and God the Father of love, a love impossible to stop, a love that had a beginning and no end. From a drawer he took out the photographs of the two children they were sponsoring, one boy, one girl. Miguel. Candace. Miguel ran into the jungle to get away from the police who rode motorcycles.

He went into the rain in his shirt and pants. Barefoot and bareheaded he walked around the yard and then out into the street. Rain pricked him like little pins. He turned the crying of his own face up into the downpour. He wanted the rain to wash him, wash the dirt out of his soul, the hardness out of the stone-dried mud of his spirit. When Ruth woke up he had returned and showered and he told her after she had eaten some breakfast. Ruth sagged and covered her eyes with her hand and locked herself in the den. Bart told their son and daughter, who had gone with them to the orphanage two years before. They crackled with words, a fire in their tongues and tears like sparks on their cheeks. Bart did not eat and did not sleep, going to the bakery at two on Monday morning, the rain tap-tapping against his skin and bones. Herman was waiting for him.

Bart stared at him. "What are you doing here?"

"Ruth called me."

"Ruth called you."

"I want to show you something."

"How to bake paska so it sells like sourdough rye?"

Herman pointed to the roof of the bakery. "Do you see that chimney? The small one?"

"What about it?"

"Did you not wonder what it was for?"

"No."

"Open the door, please, Bartholomew."

"I wish to bake alone, Herman."

"I am not going to bake. I will show you one thing. Then I am going back to bed."

"Why didn't you show me the one thing a year ago?"

"I did not think you would ever use it. Or need it."

"But this Easter Monday I suddenly do."

"Open the door, Bartholomew."

They went inside. Herman walked past the stainless steel ovens to a far wall. He had been holding a crowbar up the sleeve of his long raincoat. He smacked at the paint and plaster until he could get at the drywall. He inserted the crowbar and tugged and muttered in German and wrenched the bar sideways until a huge portion of the drywall broke away. Behind it was a stone oven.

"A long time ago we would bake the bread with a wood fire. But our orders grew larger. We needed bigger ovens. Modern ovens. We baked some loaves in the stone oven to sell as a specialty bread. Soon it was not worth it. So few purchased the bread. We had no time. Father had it covered over in 1973. Look. There is still a great bundle of dry wood inside it you can use."

"Use to do what?"

"Perhaps you will have some luck if you bake your paska in this today."

"Oh. It's a magic oven. I bake the paska using dead trees and presto! Thousands beat a path to my door."

"I myself enjoyed it when I used to bake the bread in this oven."

"Thank you, Herman. I'm sorry you came out into the storm. But I have no intention of baking paska today."

"It is still Easter."

"Oh, yes. Jesus has risen. But now it's Monday. It's his day off. Yesterday was all the big choirs and the celebrations. Now everyone's gone back to mediocrity. I am only going to bake the plain loaves today to suit the occasion. The plainest of the plain. White and soft. That is what people want, don't they, Herman? Bread without substance? Bread as light as air? It suits their religion. It is their religion."

Bart had not even intended to bake on Monday. Arnie wasn't back until Tuesday. Eleanor and Benjamin were off. No deliveries were scheduled. He stood in front of the stone oven after Herman had left. Old round stones securely mortared. The heat of Hell could not crack them. Herman's father, dead for thirty years, dead for Bart's lifetime, his fingers pressing the great stones into place.

"All right, old man," said Bart. "But only white bread today. No paska. Easter is finished."

He got the fire going red hot underneath. This would take a different skill, a skill he did not possess, to bake good bread over coals, spangled coals of orange and red and green and white and yellow and blue. There would only be a few customers. If he failed, he failed. He did not have to open the doors. He did not say he would.

He worked in the dark as the rain snapped at the windows. Fire sighed over his eyebrows and lips, over the prickle of his unshaven chin, over the nails of his fingers. He charred the first six loaves and threw them out the back door for a man with a shopping cart who rattled down the alley every morning before dawn. The next three loaves were raw in the middle. But a dozen finally emerged round and firm, baked evenly through. He tossed one into the clean wooden bin with the spoilt loaves and placed the others on the pine display shelving behind the counter. He printed a neat sign in black ink on stiff cream paper. STONE OVEN. WOOD FIRE. He baked two more dozen, flames twisting round and round his flesh and body. His mind ran clumsily over old ruts and forgotten fields of dead thistles.

We ought to have more hymns, Pastor Bart. There are not enough choruses, Pastor Bart. The organ is too fast, Reverend. The organ just grinds along, Pastor. The drums are too loud, Reverend. Where are the drums, Pastor? The children's story takes too long. Your sermons are good but twenty minutes is enough, we cannot sit forever. People will no longer come on Sunday mornings, Sunday night services would be more successful. People are not coming on Sunday nights because it is family time, Saturdays would be better. Saturday nights are social times, no wonder no one is coming out. If you have a woman in the pulpit again, we're gone and our tithe is gone with us. You need to talk more about the gifts of the Spirit, I don't think the Spirit's here, something's blocking the Spirit, there are no manifestations, no one laughs in the Spirit, no one is dancing, no one is falling in the Spirit. Reverend, if I hear one syllable in glossalalia, if I see one teardrop, if I hear any laughter, I will know God is not with your ministry. Bart, if we emphasise helping the poor too much it's a social gospel, Jesus gets lost, just concentrate on preaching the Word. Bart, what about the poor? What about the homeless? What about AIDS victims? What are we? Just a church of good words? Doesn't anyone read the Book of James anymore?

It was eight o'clock. Bart sat behind the counter on a tall wooden stool, his face dark with the heat of the stone oven. It was noon before anyone stepped into the bakery. A woman purchased three loaves of the round white bread with the faint scent of smoke in its crust. Through the afternoon, people came and went. The white loaves gradually disappeared.

What did the disciples do on Monday? They die inside on Friday. They are empty and in shock on Saturday. They are stunned by the complete turn of events on Sunday. What is there left to feel on Monday? Relief that the weekend is over? Fear of the future—if Jesus is alive again, what does that mean for all of us this week? How long and unknown did the week look when they woke up Monday morning? Yes, it would be a relief to get into the boat and do something solid and familiar again, like put up a sail or drop a net for fish. Maybe have a hot lunch and buy a loaf of bread and a wedge of cheese for supper. Maybe do nothing for once. No miracles. No crowds. No arguments with the priests. No more shocks. No more my-world-turned-upside-down-again experiences, no Samaritan tramp at a well, no thieving Zaccheus to have to love, no leper to have to touch, no devil to face in another's face, no devil to face in yourself. Thank God, for the first time in years, no having to follow Jesus, no having to try to be like him, no having to go left with him instead of right with everyone else, no having to go up when the world was going down, no unusual fishing trips or strange new stories that went over your head, no sharp words when you only meant well and wanted to protect him, no more questions answered with bigger questions, no more of his eyes that settled like whispering garnet coals in your own. You could relax. Maybe there was more coming, a whole lot more, more than you could handle. But for now he was not in the grave and not in your face. Go fishing. Eat a big supper. Sit under the stars. In case the fire was coming, the great fire that will burn you day after day, but you never die, you're Moses' bush and God is in you, and now, this week, it will begin and never stop, fire eating deeper and deeper and flaring higher and higher and no end to it for you, filled with the Sacred Name and all its bright, frightening Heaven, never killing you, and you remain for a thousand years and another thousand years and another thousand years and God never leaves his Temple, he is always there and you can't die. Better to picture him as a gardener pruning rosebushes. Better to hope he had left you alone at last. Better to daydream on Monday and pretend none of it had ever happened, that Jesus never had been. If you could live with the cold ashes and the grim setting of the Friday sun and the long Neptunian night that would ensue. Hell or Heaven, a Heaven whose fires were brighter and hotter than the fires of the damned.

Five minutes before he intended to close, a neatly dressed older man entered the bakery. He wore a long navy trenchcoat shining silver with rain, a black fedora with a slip of red feather, his grey beard was trimmed close to his skin. His glasses were brimming with water and he took them off, looking around as he rubbed them with a dry white handkerchief he had pulled from a pocket inside his coat.

"Is this Bethlehem?" he asked, speaking English with a strong accent, and Bart thought of Vienna and a man like this man standing in front of sculptured magnificence, reluctant to join a lively, fast-flowing waltz taking place in the square just beside him, the music rising and rising, the musicians seated and playing feverishly in front of a bursting white fountain of granite fish and stone mermaids.

"Yes," Bart responded. "This is Bethlehem."

"Have you any bread?"

"There is just the one loaf there."

The man returned the glasses to his eyes. "This is whole grain?"

"No. White. Unbleached."

"What is that—stoneground? Wood fire?"

"Stone oven."

The man peered around the room again looking for more shelving. "You do not have much."

"We are closing in five minutes. I had three dozen loaves."

The man bent to look in the glass counter Bart sat behind.

"What is that, please?"

Bart had not even glanced inside the counter display once during the day. He slid open the back panel and looked in from behind. A round and firm loaf of paska sat there. He groaned.

"I'm sorry. That is two days old. For all I know it's as hard as rock. I can't sell that to you."

"What sort of bread is it?"

"Paska."

"Yes. The Easter bread."

The man thought a moment, still bent over and peering in. Then he nodded and straightened, smiling at Bart. "That will be fine."

"Oh, no. I'm sorry. I can't sell that to you."

"I have good teeth."

"No."

"I must have bread. I do not like white. I will not buy the rubbish they wrap in plastic in the grocery stores. That one, please."

"I will not sell it to you."

"Please."

Bart shook his head and reached in, bringing out the loaf. It seemed to weigh four or five pounds. He held it toward the older man with both of his hands. "Take it."

"How much is that?"

"Nothing. I cannot charge you for it. Bread that's two days old. It should be out in the trash."

The man took the bread and looked at it closely. "What is on the crust? What is this design?" His fingers were touching the spikes of crust that rose from the circle of bread like nails.

"It is an Easter bread. That is meant to be the crown of thorns. The crown of thorns of Jesus Christ."

"What are those deep gashes?"

"His stripes. The scourging. Before he was crucified."

The man stared at the loaf. He suddenly gripped it tightly. He looked up at Bart, his eyes strong and flaring with tears. "Is this God? Is this my God?"

His hands trembled as he pressed his fingers through the crust. He pulled the bread so violently into his chest that Bart heard the crust crack. The man dropped to his knees and shouted, "My God! Is this you, my God?"

The man's whole body shook. He pressed the loaf harder and harder against his chest. Bart ran out from behind the counter, certain the man was about to fall backward and hit his head. It was a heart attack. He had to get the man to a chair, loosen his collar, phone for an ambulance.

"Come on. Sit over here," he urged the man, trying to lift him up from behind. But the man was as rooted as a boulder. Bart could not raise him.

"My God! My Christ! Why have I forsaken you?"

"Help me. Stand up. Come over here. There's a chair."

"Get me water. I need water."

Bart left the man kneeling and ran to the back. But the tap at the sink was not working. They were not working in the washroom either. What was going on? He grabbed an old chipped mug with a Denver Broncos logo on it and rushed out the back door. He held it under a rainpipe. The water should be clean. The storms had been washing the roof and gutters for days. The cup filled. It looked clear. He ran back inside to the old man who was shaking and blue-lipped.

"I have water. Here. Drink it."

Bart knelt beside the man and offered the cup. The man stared at him, a mad windswept eye chilling Bart's flesh, pried the loaf from his chest and tore at the crust with his fingers and nails. He broke off a piece and gave it to Bart. Another piece he held in a white fist.

"This is the body of Christ. This is the skin and bone. Eat it."

The man placed his piece in his mouth, sharp with a crusted thorn. Bart chewed and swallowed his. It was tough. His teeth could hardly bite through the crust.

"Please give me the cup," the man asked.

Bart handed him the mug. The man's hand was steady as stone.

"This is the cup of Christ. This is the blood."

He drank almost all of it, as if he had not drunk in days. He handed it back to Bart who simply held on to it. The man did not look at him. His eyes were closed. His body was still. But he said to Bart, "Go ahead."

The bit of water slipped like silver down his throat. The taste was different. Metal and tar and earth but something else. Clouds. Sky. Height. Distance. Minutes and hours and years. What? He set the cup on the floor.

The man stood up and removed his hat and trenchcoat, not a muscle quivering, as still and sure as the air in his movements. He took off his tie and shirt and his pants. Finally, he stripped off his undershirt and briefs and socks and shoes, his two gold rings, and placed his glasses on the counter. He smiled at Bart. "Do not worry. I am all right."

He stepped out the front door into the full of the lashing rain. His arms were over his head, his face lifted to the storm, and he turned around and around. His soft white body, sagging and drooping and weak, began to gleam and harden and shine like pale smooth rock glinting under the fast running water of a mountain cataract. He was smiling as he turned, slowly, slowly, his eyes shut, sometimes his lips moving, rain dripping off his short grey beard and hair. Bart got to his feet and waited. Cars drove past, slowing down, speeding on. A truck screamed past, spraying the old man with a wave of muck and dead leaves and brown water. But the storm cleansed the man's body again, pouring over him.

"I'm crazy," Bart said, "I can't do this."

But he removed his clothing and stepped into the spouts and fountains and hurricanes. At first his body rebelled, wanted to flee, but his spirit held it to its place under the clouds. Soon he welcomed the stings and kisses. Dead skin seemed to slough off him and disappear into the storm sewer. The pavement all about them crackled as the rain fell harder. Bart raised his arms and lifted his face. Eloi. Eloi. My God. My God. Why have I also forsaken you? He turned slowly, just as the old man did, seeing faces and cars and buildings and streetlamps between blurs of water and blinks of light. His ears filled with the beating of the rain. It became a rhythm and a music that drove through his bones and muscle and ligament and sinew and tissue to a core that fused all and thrust all eyes and lights and nerves and spirits and visions, the whole and all fragments of the whole, into rushing air and tumbling cloud and a spinning earth, into a borderless universe of constellations and zodiacs and ruby-eyed devils and emerald-eyed angels towering and six-winged and crushing the immensity of stars into their arms of fierce ardour, a falling into a glittering mix of vapours and geysers and nebulae and swirling dusts.

In time, Bart followed the old man back into the bakery. He locked the door and flipped the sign in the window to CLOSED. Then he walked to the stone oven and built up a fire with the last of the wood until a prism swept over them that glittered with the crystallization of their souls. Soon they were dry. The old man brought in his clothes and Bart's and they dressed before green and blue leapings and springings and flights of light. The man set his hat on his head and finally pushed his arms through the sleeves of his trenchcoat. He smiled and nodded to Bart. Their minds were far but they sensed they could embrace flesh and blood and spirit simultaneously and they did so, clutching each other, thanking God, and the old man stepped into the night and the night's soft rain.

Bart picked up the torn and gouged loaf of paska from the floor. For a moment he held it, feeling its broken crust and the bread underneath and the weight of it. Then he opened the back door and placed it in the empty wooden bin. At home he held Ruth so tightly in their bed, in their darkness, that a pain speared her side, but a good pain, a pain that drank her darkness and her crippling and her age and distortion and unbelief so that a chandelier of a thousand candles burned white and hot and this was her spirit, alive in the Easter God, the resurrected Christ.

Along the cathedral of their years, along transepts and naves and narthexes of light and dark, much came that could be touched with the hands and seen with the eyes. They gave their riches to the street children and tried to follow Jesus. Bart used only the stone oven, baking just twelve dozen loaves each day, and people came from across Denver to buy the bread since the one truck only delivered it to special cafes and bistros and restaurants. Two dozen were always set aside for Jacob's Ladder and one loaf went to the wooden bin each morning before dawn. They opened the church to all, moving from the house and into an old brick brewery that was no longer in use, which they sandblasted and hung with banners and filled with song. It seemed to them that they received five hundred souls a year for ten years and this did not diminish the Holy Spirit or their passion for Christ and indeed, they brimmed over with increasing light and fervour for God and God's world. Each family fostered at least one street child from Bogota or Mexico City or Rio de Janeiro or Sao Paulo and one orphan of the million or more orphans that was the city of Denver.

Bart dreamed it would be a perfect church but it was not. Instead, he came to see, on a night laced with nails and scourgings, that it was like a New Testament church and that he lived in St. Paul's world, among St. Paul's Christians, among St. Paul's sorrows and woundings, and he came to know also St. Paul's sheer gratefulness and his fierce prayers and the bright ecstasy of his heart. It happened without his knowledge and over much time, but Bart came to be free and his church family was large and boisterous and swollen with grace and good works, so that he must laugh, though he carried the cross of his Lord for all the seasons of the Earth.

We must set aside the cross for a time, he would tell Ruth with a smile, and sit down in the garden, the better to listen and to bring good to mind and to watch the gardener work, to catch the snatches of his songs and the whistling between his teeth as he stoops over his flowering shrubs. He can squat down beside us then, the smudges of soil dark streaks on his skin. There is time for some news, a piece of advice, perhaps, maybe a story. Then we walk again and when the way is cool and unlit and hard-scrabble, we remember him and his songs, and we can sing them after him, sing lustily in the night that spirited and full-blooded song of the redeemed.

CHAPTER 2

DAYBREAK

On that day, Sam Laurie was drinking coffee at his desk in the real estate office. It was mid-morning in September and sunlight made thick golden bars on his wall as it poured through the cracks in the venetian blinds. He glanced at their pattern under his painting of a derelict fishing boat as the light grew brighter and brighter. Suddenly, the bars flared white, as if they had become strips of burning magnesium. Sam winced and spilt his coffee.

"What is this?" he snapped and tore aside his blinds to see what was happening outside his window. Light exploded in his face and he stumbled backwards, flinging out both his arms for balance. His shirt gleamed like rolling whitecaps.

Pastor Greg Short narrowed his eyes and hissed in irritation. He had drawn the blinds tightly to keep out the morning sun so that he could pray in the cool darkness of his church office. But light was piercing the blinds and shimmering in his eyes. What were they doing outside? Was some utility truck directing powerful beams at the church building? He growled and jerked opened the blinds.

Light streamed into the room and obliterated him. He could not see anything, it was so bright and relentless. A fear pinched his heart.

"My God," he thought, "it is true."

Robin Flowers was walking her dog in the warm English evening near Balliol College at Oxford when the dusk, in a moment, became luminous, and the golden sunset spread and spread to fill the entire sky, so that it was everywhere, all around her and over her, and she looked up at the gleaming and fell, her eyes watering, and a hope sparkled in her chest as she hugged her golden lab and laughed, and it grew so bright she could not see anything except each shining hair of her dog's radiant coat.

In Beijing, a young lawyer could not sleep because of the light. He could not understand what would shine through the heavy dark curtains. Outside Nagasaki, a Buddhist monk was praying until the light flickered off his fingertips and his robe. He went to the door of the temple, afraid it was a great fire or a terrible bomb, and the light fastened onto him and ignited him and blinded him, so that he was all colours but he did not know it.

Over the entire Earth people woke from sleep thinking it was the moon or the stars or a great blaze. Others stood in an unending daylight and looked until it was too painful for them to look any longer. In all the world, the light took people's sight and drove them to their knees and darted through every bone, every ligament, every blood vessel, every fibre of their being. Traffic had no choice but to stop. Planes flew and flew into textures of gold and silver. The snowgoggles of the Himalayan climber could not dim the glare, nor could the Rae-Bans of the sunworshipper on the beach. It was impossible for armies to see and shoot any longer. The rapist and the murderer were paralyzed in the shining and all victims were hidden from harm. Presidents and premiers and prime ministers and kings froze, but a dying woman in Africa, dressed only in muddy rags, climbed to her feet and closed her eyes and smiled and began to dance slowly in the fiery dust. Beasts lay down where they stood. Dolphins and grey whales leaped out of water that roared silver and green with a light that would not stop, a light that swelled and swelled with intensity.

I stood on the spotted lawn by my house with my daughter and my son and my wife, a rake in my hands. Golden leaves dropped over our shoulders and onto the grass. The children stared at the glittering house and trees and creek, while my wife and I shaded our eyes and cringed. Then they looked up and, breaking into great child smiles of recognition and delight, ran together across the lawn, waving and calling, "Hi, hi," and shouting back to us, "Mom, Dad, look," and jumping as they ran and laughing. And his laughter coming too, shot through with light, sounding like thunder to some, and to others like the great breakers of the great seas, but to the rest of us simply the bright laughter of an honest man who had known much love and given much love, who basked in and treasured the friendship and adoration of all the generations of all the children, who looked at the mornings to come and found each one of them to be very good.

CHAPTER 3

THE PRAYER TREE

THE TRAIL CURLED UP the hill to a ridge and Sam Willow would hike along the spine of the ridge until he found the Ponderosa pine. Coming up the trail from the lake, it was all summer aspen and poplar and round green leaves and the sharp scent of fresh bark. By August, the whole hillside filled the nostrils with the tang of baked evergreen, the warm, rich bite of pine needles, it draped over everything like a fine light linen. In those weeks, Sam often thought of a four poster bed in the forest, made up with fresh white sheets and pillows, in which he could sleep and be awakened only by a red squirrel darting over the quilt of hunter green. That, he thought, would be a true peace. But he went on to the ridge each time and made his way to the tree that was mostly branches now, tufts of green needles here and there, blasted and scoured by the big mountain winds into limbs of silver and pewter, arms running and looping and twisting and knotting and praying, my God, leaping out. He sat under the tree on slabs of rock spattered with bright orange lichen. He came on the tough days and gazed at the blue peaks to the west, tall snowbrushed rock that knew nothing of his pain and would remember nothing of him in a hundred years, and so were safe. Grasshoppers clicked and whirred. He might see a hawk or an eagle floating on the back of the cirrus. In autumn, the elk would squeal and grunt below him in a valley, but he would never see them. Ants and spiders and beetles scuttled over his boots and over his legs and he let them. All of us are created, he thought. We share that. Fashioned by the same God. It is the point at which we are truly one.

Once, over the mountains and further south, Sam had been part of a pastoral team that ministered to over twenty thousand people. For several years they had experienced what everyone else called a revival, a powerful touch of the Holy Spirit. Sam called it God's terrible swift sword, for where this experience was most real, it cut people right open to expose every secret, every fault, every perversion. But most did not want to go there. They danced and shook and screeched and laughed and fell and lay dead. "Husha husha" services, he called them, after the ancient child's rhyme. He tried to be as honest to God as he could be in the middle of it all, but it was a carnival, it was an Orlando of the soul, a Las Vegas of all the senses, and after awhile he could not tell what was real and what was not, or when he was truly Sam Willow or another man. So he left.

A few of the leaders pronounced judgement over his unfaithfulness, cowardice and betrayal, but he welcomed the thunderbolt at that point and left anyway, hoping it might fall and end his confusion. Instead he brought his confusion to the mountains and foothills and to a small village that already had seven churches, where he started an eighth, a church for those who wanted to struggle, he told the people that came. Few stayed. If they did not want a Carnival God they wanted One that was readily available, with an instruction booklet that was easy to understand. Life was hard enough. No one wanted a complex God and a faith riddled with conundrums and enigmas. Mediocrity was preferable to a painful challenge to depth. An easily recognizable and popular Christian movement, replete with catchwords and repetitive phrases and shouted and predictable sermons, was infinitely preferable to a pastor that asked questions, and who demanded that you think, and wrestle with the angel of God night after night, until God finally changed your name.

The sun was higher, it was getting warm, Sam pulled a large old tin mug from his daypack, went over to a nearby stream that was perpetually fed by an ancient glacier, and sat back down, taking a long drink. Well, who could blame them? You fought the government, you fought your boss, sometimes you fought your wife and kids, did you want to fight God too? Who needed to mine ore that deep when you could pan goldust out of the river bed? Who wanted a name like Israel, who wanted to name their firstborn God-Struggler Jones?

There on the hill, under the writhing pine, he could imagine things worse than they were. His wife often pointed out the good in every place they had been. Yes, the bad could be found and unearthed again and again, she said. But there lay all the bright shining things in plain view and Sam, with his eyes scanning the ground for dirt, never saw them. In all the books, churches went from six to six thousand in a handful of years. People were saved with one presentation of the gospel. Children were healed of deadly diseases by one or two prayers. Few mentioned the struggle. Perhaps the struggle did not sell books. People wanted a quick and easy success, a microwave Christianity, a pentium faith. Sam shrugged and sipped at his cup of cold water. It was time to remember St. Paul.

In Pisidian Antioch, it was spiritual women with high reputations and men with political clout who went after Paul and Barnabas for preaching about Jesus. They threw the two of them out. At Iconium, they were threatened with a stoning and ran to Lystra where the crowd really did stone Paul and almost killed him. They did not come up with a health and wealth gospel out of these experiences. "We must go through many hardships to enter the kingdom of God." What always struck Sam, as he went through this litany under the naked pine tree, was that Paul took suffering as a given, part of the package of his Christian faith, where Christians in the West now saw suffering as a source of confusion and a trigger to doubting the presence and the commitment of God. What if at a pastor's first few church plants he was threatened, mobbed and beaten at every one? And what if he went from one to another in the space of a few months? Even if small churches were planted in each city, would the mission board of the denomination continue to back a pastor with such a wild track record?

Paul had tried to get into Asia twice in the early days and couldn't. Luke wrote that it was the Holy Spirit that blocked them. After raising all the funds and support and getting all the Bibles and gospel literature printed in Asian? After pumping up the whole team that it was Asia For Christ? Then Paul tosses and turns and has a dream about going to Macedonia. So off they go. Sorry, boys, change of plans. That's God, you know, up and down and all around. They wind up in Philippi, where—after bringing Lydia and her family to Christ—they get beaten up, whipped and jailed. Out of that mess, the jailer and his family become Christians, and then the team heads out to Thessalonica. They get caught up in a riot and have to sneak out of the city at night. They go to Berea. The crowds turn against them. So Paul moves on to Athens and Corinth. He winds up staying in Corinth a year-and-a-half. He stops in Ephesus for two years. A riot blows up there too, a big one.

What do you do with this man? Everywhere he goes people—or nature—beat him up. They hit him with the thirty-nine lashes five times. They stone him. They beat him with rods three times. Three times a mission ship goes down under him. He struggles a day and a night to survive in the open sea, clinging to a bit of wreckage. Rivers try to drown him. Bandits try to rob him. There's never enough money, never enough food, never enough sleep. The work never gets easier. It breaks his back but he keeps on going. More jail terms. More prison sentences. Even Christians hate him. And the happy ending for our hagiography? Nero chops off his head.

What a Christian success story. What a testimony to use in promoting your brand of multi-level marketing. Once I was Saul, now I am Paul, look at what God has done for me. Get a good look at these rags—triple stitching in the seams. And take a look at these scars. You too can have this abundant life. Just give your soul to Jesus.

Sam squinted as the sun moved farther west and into his line of sight. He pressed the cold mug against the side of his warm face. How many mission boards would want a man with a track record like Paul's? Let's give him three years in New York and see what he does with it. Another riot! This doesn't look good for the denomination. Drop him. Get him out of here. Find someone stable to rally the converts he picked up. We need some credibility. If God's in it, there's no riots.

Sam leaned his head back against the tree's silver trunk. That was it, wasn't it? Paul and the others just did what they did. They said what they said. If only two people came to Christ, they weren't dismayed. If someone broke their legs, they crawled on their arms. No surprise. No, "Oh, my God, I knew it, you've abandoned us, you don't exist, THERE'S NO GOD!" Songs at midnight with the chains biting into your ankles and your back stinging and blood-crusted.

St. Paul squats with Sam under the gnarled pine tree and pops figs into his mouth. What did you expect, Samuel? Jesus bled. Why wouldn't his disciples bleed too? It's a vicious world, by choice. You think they're going to smile and say, Thanks, I needed to hear that, when you talk about sin and hell and blood and fire it just makes me want to love your sweet Jesus? Where is it written that God's people just cruise on through, Samuel? Where is the person who spoke words that mattered who didn't suffer? Who planted an easy church? Who lived in palaces with silk pyjamas and strawberries in cream when they stood up for Jesus? Why do you expect years of trouble-free ministry? And then when you don't get them, you think God can't be God and you throw away your faith? We knew

they'd whip us, Samuel. We knew we'd die. We knew only a handful might
believe us. We did it because it was right, not a sensible lifestyle choice.

The mountains rumbled down and down and petered out somewhere
in New Mexico. Sam had seen the back of a wolf once, moving with the
trot that made it look as if it were going sideways, but wasn't. A cow
moose had charged him to protect her calf. Only a grove of poplar had
saved his life. The cow chased him from trunk to trunk and finally gave
up and left him to return to her calf. He'd never seen a grizzly or a cougar,
but he'd run into black bear a dozen times. They always ran away or scuttled up a tree. Of course, he'd had his dogs with him too. They had coy-
ote blood and he wondered if other animals scented the wildness in them.

They were small down in the valley, down in Legacy, the smallest
he'd ever pastored, fifteen or twenty after one year of going flat out. It
seemed the older he got, the harder it got to fake anything. And the more
he acted with integrity, the smaller his congregations became. He wasn't
mean-spirited, but he wasn't about to preach sermons that left his people
free under God to be nothing. The few of them got their hands dirty at the
women's shelter, at the soup kitchen, they took in the scattered homeless
that passed through their town. They drank coffee with their friends and
broke the great Western taboo of the 21st century, they mentioned Christ.

Was that a mountain goat picking its way up a slope? No easy job.
Maybe to the goat it was easy, having the feet for it. Sam walked over and
dipped his tin cup in the stream. The sun perched on the mountain range
like an eagle. Soon Sam would go down and read to his kids. Then he'd
sit with his wife while she read to him. They might make love under the
love of God and he would feel better about his life and ministry and curl
up for sleep, cracking the window for the cool breezes. Dawn could be red
or gold. He would stare at it and then rise and try to put together the pieces
of the puzzle of the day and of the ages.

Before the twenty thousand plus church, there had been lots of little
churches. He'd seen people come back to life, seen dreams come true,
seen prayers soar and return with a brightness of doves. Maybe he should
have stayed in one place like some did, stayed for thirty years, instead of
all the nickel-dime stuff, breaking up hard ground, the plough leaping in
his hands and the harness cutting like a whip into his back, the heavy horses thudding across the earth, rocks spitting from the ploughshare like flot-
sam from a cleaving of the sea. Well, but if you did just the one church,

you never saw the souls from the other ones down the line. It was a different life, a different world, and who was to say you weren't supposed to be the soil turner and rock pitcher and seed caster?

Sam laughed. St. Paul bragged about his suffering, the more faith he had the more he got hit. How many people would that impress nowadays? What Paul really wanted to brag about was the Cross, how great it was, how great Jesus was. The Cross was the wonderful dark door to knowing God. Jeremiah said that was all God cared about. Do you understand me, Sam? Do you know who I really am? Do you know that I love to do what is kind? That I love justice? I get up and dance to that stuff. Do you know that, Sam?

A few times I think I've had ahold of it, and a few times I've lost my grip, Father of lights. Sometimes I wonder how many of us pastors stick to ritual and routine, long after we've lost sight of you, just so we've got something to keep running with that's familiar to us? When you're fifty-seven, you can't let go, it's too close to retirement. So you work your sermons and your orders of service and all your patterns of ministry, that's where your strength comes from, your theology and your work habits, but you, Father, where are you, who knows? I almost left you for good when Richard died. Out hunting squirrels with his brother Kevin. We were all there. Looking and looking. Kevin draws a bead and squeezes the trigger just as Richard jumps up and points, "I see one!" That .22 bullet exploded in the back of his brain. He was still alive in my arms. I ran and ran with him until Mom got up to me with the jeep and I jumped in. I prayed and I prayed and I prayed, oh, my God, but you didn't do it, you didn't do anything, it was like nails going up and in. Was it supposed to make me happy that Kevin became a Christian because of all that, Kevin the hell-raiser, was that the way it was meant to be on earth, just as it was meant to be in heaven, Kevin shoots Richard, Richard goes to heaven, Kevin gets broken and he comes to you and that's the only way you could work it? One dies so the other lives? I went through Richard's journals, full of you, all full of you, day after day, year after year. I took his calligraphy set and I sat down and I learned to put some of his poems and prayers down on parchment, Celtic lettering, like his books of the Irish and Scottish and Welsh Christians and their songs and blessings.

Then I took a leave of absence and we rented a farmhouse and I painted all those crazy signs: THE HARVEST IS PAST AND WE ARE NOT

SAVED; THE WAGES OF SIN IS DEATH; JUDGMENT DRAWETH NIGH. I nailed those signs to the sides of a big farm truck and I'd drive it into the city and park it all over the place, knowing people were looking and reading. Janitor-green pants. Janitor-green shirt. Tractor cap. Grew a beard. Wore glasses. Month after month, driving into the city, parking anywhere I could, leaving it there all day while I drank coffee and struck up weird end-of-the-world conversations. As if you used our Gregorian calendar. As if you loved those signs. We go through so many phases as a kid and we think it's done, but then we go through all those phases as a man. What I thought I knew when I was fifteen, when I was twenty, or thirty, when I was married, when I had kids, my first church, my second church, feeling you inside when I worshipped like a rushing cataract of light, none of it's left, there's nothing I know.

Who are you? Why did there have to be so much blood? Why Jesus' blood? Why the martyrs' blood? Why all the hatred for us? Why all the violence? What difference does it make to you? Why do you need it? Why does sin need it? What good does it do? Richard's blood was all over me.

Why did you bother putting us through this? Why did you even birth us? In every family, in every country, something breaks down. You're God. It could have been anything. Why the dying? Why all the hurting? Why this world? Why like this?

Soft clouds in the west were full of battle fire. But quickly the fire went out. The stars began to climb up their tall ladders and at the top they lit their candles. Sam felt he was in a cathedral, but overhead there was no stone, only the candlelight and the long black arches. *If I walked up there I would know, wouldn't I? I would know something.*

He poured the rest of his water on the ground. He could still see the mountains. Did they change in the dark? He looked at the agonized limbs of the pine tree. *You would be like any other pine except the wind stripped you bare and beat you and now you are more wonderful than all the others.*

Sam walked past the tree and down the looping path. The lake was a black, breathing thing. He stopped along its shore and smelled the cool wetness of the water and the fresh greenness of the plants that grew near it. His truck came to him white and sudden in the gravel parking lot at the end. He leaned against it. No moon. New moon. A mallard drake flapped its wings on the water, said something, and settled back down. Sam scanned the shoreline. No cabin lights lit. No campfires. Nothing in the huge darkness.

He was exhausted, but a charred stick gleamed inside, a wind fanned it and passed over and it continued to glisten. A great horned owl flew across the stars, so big, wings fully extended in a smooth and swift glide, and it called, Who? Who are you? Who are you? Who are you?

CHAPTER

A TOURIST IN MOAB

WHEN THE RADIATOR BLEW on the old Chevy Blazer Dirk got out and left it behind, white steam spraying from under its hood, sucked up almost instantly by the dry desert air. He slung a pack heavy with water bottles over one shoulder and started walking south and west. His shirt and pants were a beige khaki. So was his broad-brimmed hat, full of creases and sitting disjointed on his head, having been crammed up where the dash met the windshield for several days. His hiking boots crunched over sand and gravel, his sunglass frames stabbed light. In five minutes the Blazer was an orange rock behind him, trying to blend with the yellows and purples and reds of cliff and boulder.

The heat eventually made his walking sluggish. He slumped in the shade of a tall Joshua tree and slowly drained a litre bottle of water. He had seven bottles left. That gave him three days, he figured. He had some apples and bread and beef jerky. It would have to be enough. He removed his glasses. The sun bit at his eyes.

The burning of Sarah scorched him. He ground a fist into his forehead. No. I will not think of that. A big man, William Arnolds, the deacon, was shouting and his skin was bubbling and blistering. Stained glass exploded.

Dirk stared hard at the small green lizard that darted onto his boot and froze. What new reality is this? he asked the lizard. You climbed onto it. Does it feel good to you? Would you make a home here? Raise babies? But the mountain moves—Dirk shifted his foot. Now what? The lizard slipped under a rock. Yes. I am looking for the same thing.

Dad! Jesus! Daddy!

Dirk took a bottle that was still cold and dumped water down the back of his neck. The shock stopped the voice. Water struck along the spine and into his pants. Now there were six bottles.

Pour them all out, down your back, on the sand like David. Speed things up. Take control. Get it over with. Dirk had his hand in the pack on the bottles but he pulled out an apple instead, a bright green Granny Smith, and chewed on it.

He had driven from Baltimore to Moab in Utah, stopping only for gas or to use a washroom. Moab had been full of tourists in good humour. The locals saw Dirk as just another one of the crowd, but Dirk could not bear the tourists' joviality and their freedom. He stayed inside his motel room and slept for a night and a day. Then he left Moab and its cheerful multitudes behind him and steered his 4X4 past the red stone arches and into the huge stars of a desert night. That was two days ago. Now he was on foot. Good. Nothing better.

The sun beat on his back and shoulders with heavy gold bars as he made his way through the desert again. Dirk's pace was much slower now. The sun looked to be at about one o'clock. He had smashed his watch with a small ochre stone in Moab.

What is it about the English? he asked himself. We grow up in green fields with hedges and oaks and mists and soft grey skies. Then we constantly hurl ourselves into heat-intense environments. India. Australia. The Caribbean. The American West. How many English and Irish and Scots had died with Custer in the June heat of eastern Montana? And there was Arabia too, and Lawrence, and Palestine, and Egypt, and Gordon of Khartoum dying there in the Sudan, and Burma and Singapore. And Dirk Green of Nottinghamshire, another one of the lads who had crossed the ocean to seek his fortune.

A hawk, two hawks circled far ahead. He had never seen one dive, though he once watched one jigging and jagging after a darting swallow, never capturing it. The hawks drifted on to the west. Dirk followed.

His water was gone the evening of the second day. He'd consumed five litres and the other bottle he had thrown at the devils jabbering and springing from his head onto the red and purple rocks. The water seemed to dissolve them. Perhaps it was holy water. He began to walk at night.

The first time he slept well during the day under an overhang of rock. But he staggered through the second night until dawn gouged his eyes and he collapsed under a stunted Joshua tree that offered little relief from the sun.

All morning the heat battered him. By noon he still had not slept deeply and was balled up into a hand's span of shadow.

Now you are going to die.

Very well. Get on with it.

Die. Die. Die.

Good. Good. Good.

He forced himself to get up and walk in the daylight but it was more like stumbling and it seemed to him that he moved in and out of snapping and dancing heat.

Flames fell over him. Sarah is rolling. And little Ginger. And Bobby. The fire is stained glass. Peter and Paul, why are they dying? Why are my wife and children dying? Why are they dying again? First, you kill them with water. Then you promised never to use water again. So it was fire the second time. Burnt hair and burnt nails and burnt skin. Now the flames are in my mouth and shooting out of my eyes and the devils are screaming like monkeys.

Dirk! Dirk!

Ow! Ow! Daddy!

Fires ran up and down his arms and legs and back and his hair vanished in an orange flash.

The sun set and the flames stopped. Dirk fell against a rock, his lips cracking. A cup of cold water, Jesus. Let me die. I am no better than anyone else. How many Christians did you kill in the death camps because they would not kiss the toes of the SS? How many Jews did you kill? That missionary to the Stoney Indians, why did you kill him? After all he had done for your Name? Coming home across the plains and you send him a blizzard. He cannot see. He walks in circles and prays to you. He dies. All the ones in the death camps died. How many did you let Idi Amin slaughter? How many did you let the Khymer Rouge kill? I am not braver than they are. I don't have more faith. I do not preach better sermons. I do not pray more hours. Kill me, too. I won't lose my faith, if that's what you're worried about. Even though you slay me, yet will I trust you.

His head throbbed for an hour before the cool night calmed all. His tongue was thick and swollen, like a wad of felt, he could not eat the jerky or the bread. He found a last orange and bit it, squeezing the warm juice down his throat. It stung his lips like wasps. He lay flat on the sand. The stars dropped closer.

It had been the best week of his ministry, anywhere, anytime. He had successfully promoted a dry grad celebration as an alternative to the high school drunks common to their end of Baltimore. Five hundred grads had shown up and partied all night without a drop of beer or a dime bag of crack. One hundred and twenty had given their lives to Christ. The church had prayed them through it all for months and was closer knit than ever before. It was a great Sunday. Sarah in a dress as blue as the South Pacific. Bobby clinging to his arm and jumping as they walked and asking him questions about what they would do during the summer. Ginger tottering along next to Sarah, a new red dress, new white shoes, a green purse. He was just going to say something funny in his sermon when four bottles stuffed with burning rags crashed through the stained glass windows of Paul and Peter and James and John. The carpet erupted. The pews erupted. The hymn books erupted. And nine people. He burnt his hands trying to reach Sarah and Bobby and Ginger. One whole side of the church became a fireball. He rolled Bobby on the carpet. Sarah was trying to tumble away from the flames. And just as he reached out for Ginger her face and hair ignited and she screamed into his eyes.

The teens that had thrown the bottles had been high and part of a gang that was furious with Dirk for messing up their grad drunk. Of the nine people that caught fire that Sunday morning only one survived. They buried the others after a packed funeral service of music and testimony. What saw him through that? Where did the words come from? Fifteen years of public speaking or the Holy Spirit? Was the dry grad worth eight lives, worth his wife and his daughter and his son? Why had he pushed it? For Jesus? For the kids? For himself and his ministry? The Reverend Dirk Green, Most Holy, pastor of Lord of Lords, Baltimore. Was it for the church growth he hoped to attract? Or had it truly been for the Kingdom of God?

"They're not mutually exclusive, you know, Dirk," the quiet man from denominational headquarters had said.

"Aren't they?" Dirk had shot back. "If you say certain things, make certain stands, your church will have all kinds of new people dropping by to check you out. But if you say and do certain things that Jesus did in certain places, people won't flock to your doors. You're rocking the boat. Others may thank you for your moral backbone. You may make a difference to the moral fibre of your neighbourhood. But your church won't grow because of it. You might get only a few hardy souls. Most will never come."

"You don't have to be controversial to advance the Kingdom of God."

"Right. It's the 21st century. How can you talk about Jesus anymore without being controversial? A Christian can't be anything but controversial."

"Just get converts, Dirk. That's all that matters. Bring people to Jesus."

"Whose Jesus? Which Jesus? The multi-level marketing Jesus? The status quo Jesus? The jolly Jesus? The Santa Claus Jesus? The healthy, wealthy and wise Jesus? Or how about the one with the whip in his hand?"

"Dirk. We're asking you to take a six month leave of absence. We're requiring it. Go on a holiday. Buy a beach towel. Fly to Hawaii and be a tourist. Just get away from Baltimore."

"Are you trying to get rid of me? In case I rock the boat again and get some more people killed? I'm not great PR for the denomination, am I?"

"Dirk, what you've had to go through is terrible. Just get away and clear your head. We'll take care of the finances. Your paycheque will be deposited to your account automatically at the first of the month."

"What a relief."

"If you need someone to meet you somewhere and talk, just phone. Wherever you are."

"Bora Bora? Timbuctoo?"

"Wherever, Dirk."

"Do you think my family are martyrs for Christ? Do you think they died for the gospel? Or do you think they're martyrs to my ego?"

"Dirk, stop beating yourself up. You didn't know what that gang was going to do."

"Do you think I would have pulled out of the dry grad even if I had known about the gang?"

"I don't know."

"I wonder why a lot of our support outside of Lord of Lords comes from people that aren't Christians? I think it's because most of the churches don't have any guts. They save people to beef up their numbers. But they don't turn their converts into anything. There's no morality. It doesn't matter what you do. Just believe in Jesus and it's covered. No talk about right and wrong. No good and evil. That could upset somebody. Save them to nothing. Jesus is a glass of milk. He pacifies. And the churches grow and grow. But the world never changes because the Christians aren't really changed."

"All right, Dirk. I have to get going. You take care of yourself."

"No, I'll tell you what it is. The churches killed my family. They wouldn't back us. They wouldn't stand with us. They resented us for causing all the fuss. What's a little alcohol abuse? Just get people saved and shut up. If Christians had stood with us those kids wouldn't have dared bomb our church. One of them was from a Baptist church for pity's sake. I could write a book: *Christianity for Cowards.* You never have to change when you come to Christ. Just become more of a coward. It would be a bestseller. I should write it on my required leave of absence. Did you say I have six months to fix myself?"

They stood quietly in front of him just before sunrise, Sarah, Bobby and Ginger, shoulder to shoulder. They flickered silently, their whole bodies were flame, but they did not burn up. They were perfectly composed. Their gazes were steady as a flat calm on a windless sea. Their eyes and faces were strong.

Are you accusing me too? Are you joining the devils?

But it was not exactly an accusation, was it? They wanted him to be, what? Stronger? To go on? To love God? What?

His mouth was dry and full of pain. He tucked a small stone inside one cheek and it helped a little saliva to flow. The colour he walked slowly into made him think someone had tipped over a crate of oranges and slashed them with a long sharp silver knife. It ran over his head and eyes and fingers. With a puff of morning wind the heat came. A razor cut into the skin of his cheeks and forehead, right down into the bones of his arms. He stumbled forward, eventually sliding his feet, scarcely picking them up. He fell, got up, fell. It was noon. He gave up.

Kill me.

He rose on all fours. His sunglasses were gone. His eyes were close to the sand. He thought he saw the sharp edges of a print, a small print, the steps of an animal. Crawling, he followed the tracks. He did not care about the sharp pains in his knees and palms. He came to a thin stream of water that emerged from a rock, ran a few yards, then disappeared under another rock. The sand was churned up. Lowering his lips, he drank. He would stop, wait, then drink again. After about ten minutes he lay down by the stream with his head on his arms and slept. Huge boulders blocked the knife heat.

Cheers, Rachel.

How are you keeping, Dirk?

I am travelling.

Still restless? Still the nomad?

Well, it's not a permanent state. I'm a tourist. You?

I'm planted.

Is it like they say?

This place? Of course, it's lovely, Dirk. Did you think it would disappoint too?

Who knows anything anymore?

No, it's really wonderful. You should see how happy Rebecca is here.

Is she?

Oh, Dirk, yes. It's been grand for her. She's so healthy. You ought to see the colour in her cheeks. Are you thinking of coming up for a visit?

I might.

You'd be welcome.

Just like I am? Welcome?

Could you really believe otherwise?

I don't know anymore.

Something sniffed him and he opened his eyes and looked and there was sand and there was nothing. He drank some more and then sat up, pressing his back into a cool boulder. The sun was at six o'clock. He would rest here a night and a day and then move on. Chilled, he reached into the small pack he still had with him. One blanket. He pulled it over himself and soon the evening star glittered overhead.

Rachel had been his first wife, Rebecca his first child. A long time ago in England, in the long green fields and mists and the pink roses. A country church. A parsonage almost five hundred years old, stone, ringed with ivy. A garden of flowers that brimmed over the flagstone path, saucered with the steps of ladies from the days of John Donne and John Bunyan. Rachel was ecstatic. But he had his problems with the congregation. He wanted to change the world and they wanted to live comfortably in it. They wanted to go home to a hot Sunday lunch, happy with their ingestion of God until the following Sabbath. He grew angry and depressed.

"Look," she said one afternoon, "I'm taking Rebecca with me to Mom's. I'll be back inside a fortnight. You need some quiet to pray and think. We'll talk some more when we get back together. If we have to move on, we'll move on. But I'll be taking the parsonage and the perennials with us."

She laughed and kissed him on the cheek. A day later she was dead. Rachel had been first off the ferry. As she drove forward, inexplicably, the ferry backed away from the dock. The van drove off the ferry ramp and sank in fathoms of cold dark water. Neither Rachel or Rebecca ever surfaced. Divers had to find them. Rachel was in the back seat with Rebecca who was still strapped into her car seat.

He had gone up to Oxford to stay with a friend. He cried for several days and then became numb, he could not feel pain or pleasure. Members of a church home group prayed over him and someone muttered that Dirk's soul was a steel vault. In a few months he was on his way to America, invited to minister at a large church in New York. One year led to another and led to Sarah who he called a gift of resurrection. The children brought him to God once again in a way no prayers or books or worship had been able to do.

Now it was another night. He lurched along under a shard of moon. His water bottles were full. He would drink a litre every day, no more. That would get him somewhere, perhaps to a cave. Long before dawn he was exhausted. He pushed himself to a small canyon where he clambered down among some brush and cactus and rock, hoping he would find enough shade once the sun rose. He slept. There were no dreams.

Before another week was over his water was gone and all his stale bread and jerky. His head ached constantly and his tongue was swollen again. He decided to walk during the day and let the sun have a go at him, perhaps finish him off. He slept a day and a night and then began to walk once more under the cloudless flaming sky. He did not get far. His legs buckled and he collapsed in a vast expanse of sand. His two wives, Sarah and Rachel, walked hand-in-hand toward him and his three children were playing and shouting and building sand castles with yellow shovels and red plastic buckets.

Please, God. Kill me.

He lay on his stomach in the hot sand and had no strength to get up. He did not want to take his own life but he was glad to let the desert do the job. The heat slammed and slammed against his back. Get on with it. Get it over with. Sand worked its way into his mouth and he was a child at Brighton again and he was eating the stuff along with the ice cold lolly he had dropped on the beach.

There is no morality. It is all novelty and sensation. The churches are Vanity Fair and we are dazzled by all the lights and the rides and the loud music. But it makes no difference to the real world. Christianity has become an escape, an illusion, smoke and mirrors, a narcotic.

An opiate, perhaps?

I'm serious. We do not love, we lust.

Forgive me, but I wonder if you're coming up with all this to assuage your guilt over Baltimore. You know the promotion of a dry grad wasn't worth your family's lives, let alone the other five who died.

Is Jesus worth their lives? If they were killed because they followed Jesus would it be worth it?

That's another matter.

We tried to stop the substance abuse, to offer an alternative to madness and death.

That's not Jesus.

You mean Jesus wouldn't go there?

You weren't standing for Jesus. You were standing for an idea. Or a program. Whatever you wish to call it. But it wasn't the gospel.

So the gospel can't take you there?

It wasn't the gospel. It was you.

Are you telling me the gospel can't take you to morality?

The gospel is above all that.

I need to find some water.

Or what?

I'll die.

I thought you wanted to die.

I do.

You want to stay alive because you think you might see God. What better place than a desert?

He staggered on for an hour that night and came to a cairn. It was built up over something. He pushed the stones away. There was a canvas bag stencilled U.S. ARMY covering a jerry can of water. Five gallons. Tepid. Brackish. Why had they stuck it out here? How long ago? He drank and almost threw up.

Keep the water in. Keep the moisture in. You might see God any day now.

Next to the can of water he found a dozen ready-to-eat meals in airtight packages. He decided to fill his water bottles and camp out by the boulders nearby until he had eaten all the food and drunk all the water in the jerry can. He stayed eight days. Stronger than he had felt in weeks he resumed his journey, walking in the cool of the nights, the stars tangled in the wild hair sprouting over his head and face.

Angels spoke with him. Some with eyes like crystal. Others no more than walking fire. One evening he saw clouds banked as high as blue mountain peaks in the west but by the time they reached him they had been broken to pieces and only bits as large as a man's hand scattered over him. Nothing stopped the spears of sun that mangled his body and his spirit. He reached a desert expanse as flat as prairie where there was no shade to huddle under. He could only sleep a few hours and then it seemed better to walk again rather than be spitted and turned under yellow fire. There came a moment when he thought he was still moving across the desert but a fragment of him knew that he was not, that his legs had ceased once and for all, that there was gravel in his mouth, that he lay on his back, that the sun nipped and ripped and gnawed, that he would die soon and that he was glad.

He sensed a shadow, a something, a someone. A scraping near his ear. Was it angel or beast? He was certain he saw the blue gleam of a rifle barrel.

"Shoot me," he said.

But he woke again and the sun lay in a friendly fashion across his sheets from a skylight. His body felt washed and every bone well rested. The hair had been shaved from his head and face. It seemed to him that he had eaten and been given clean water to drink. There was a bathroom near the bed. He got up, became dizzy, rested a moment, then stepped across cool brown tiles to the toilet.

The man's name was Max. He had built the adobe house five years before. No, he was not squatting. The land was leased and he was supposed to be raising goats. But he had come out here because of Y2K.

"There were as many as twenty of us at one time," he told Dirk over a breakfast of oatmeal and oranges. "The place is compact but it has a lot of rooms below ground. Huge water tanks. I drive a water truck out here once a month. Used to be once a week. We use the water over and over. Finally, I water a little garden with it. With fresh tomatoes in my stomach I can take on anything."

"Where are the others now?"

"Back to civilization. Civil-lies-nation. We were all from a church, you heard of King of Kings? Split the church, split marriages. When it was 2001 and still nothing much had happened, we began to quarrel. People left. I told my friends I had no interest in going back to civil-lies-nation. My wife took the kids out to San Diego. Here I sit. Lots of food and drink. Plenty of sunshine. The feds don't bother me. I still have the goats too."

"I found water once under a cairn of stones."

"U.S. ARMY? That was us. There's little places all over the desert hereabouts. Survival caches. In case something happened here at the main compound."

Over the next few weeks Dirk got to know the brown adobe building well, prepared meals for the two of them, became a goatherd. Standing near a thin stretch of coarse grass as the black-haired goats crunched and tore, he expected a bush to burn. Once two fighter jets streaked overhead but they were flying high.

Max never prodded. Sipping coffee on the deck one night and counting stars Dirk told him. Max, long and lean and one with the desert with his shaven head and brown khaki and dusty skin, poured them each a fresh cup and sighed.

"I wish the world had ended. I can't go back. It's pretty lonely here. But you're heading on, aren't you?"

"I'm looking for a cave."

"There are lots of caves."

"One near water. One that takes forty days to reach from Moab."

"Forty days? How long have you been walking?"

"I'm not sure. I rested here and there."

"When were you in Moab?"

"June seventh or eighth."

"I found you on July fourth. That gives you another ten or twelve days."

"Do you know the desert well?"

"As well as any man. Look. There's a bit of an oasis. We scouted all around here in '99, leaving water and food caches, checking out caves. This one we stuck guns and ammo and food into. It would have been a kind of last stand place. There's even clothing and blankets. Books. A regular library. We called it one of our cities of refuge."

"Are you telling me I can go there?"

"You can go wherever you like. But if you still want to die, stay away from the oasis."

"Mornings I want to die. Afternoons I want to see God."

"The desert has a lot of gods."

"How long would it take me to walk to this oasis?"

"I can drive you there in less than a day."

"But walking?"

"Ten."

"So it's the place."

"You think so?"

"You're the angel that saved my life. You ought to know."

Max laughed. "I wonder if you'll come back to Eshkol, Dirk?"

"Maybe. I don't have anything to go back to."

"There'll always be a room. Plenty of diesel for the generators. Lots of food. I'll grill you a stack of hotcakes when you get back from God."

"You think he'll meet me out there?"

Max shrugged. "He'll meet you where he wants. Never where we want."

Dirk wore fresh khaki, a new hat and boots, packed plenty of water and food, and carried a compass and a map. Max stood watching and Dirk saw him and Eshkol dissolve in the shimmers of heat as if they had never been. He walked over the burning stones. After a few days he felt alone. Max's fault. He did not want to die but he wanted to see God now with the firmness of desert granite, the fire of desert heat.

At night once, working his way through a bag of overripe fruit, he wondered if Max truly existed. If he retraced his steps would he find a man and an adobe house or ruins and a skeleton? Cool breezes moved sand all around him. He pulled out the old point blanket Max had lent him and wrapped himself in it.

"Where are you God?"

Fresh breezes, fresh starfire.

"I have nowhere else to go but to the end."

The mountain was easy to spot when he was still three days away from it. Hawk nose. Heavy eyebrows. Sharp cheekbones. Up a skinny trail past the lips. What had lived there? Max was lifting up the palms of his hands. A big cat. Men. A long, long time ago. Everything in the desert is a long, long time ago.

He did not even climb up and go inside the cave. He drank from the small pool of water that seeped out of the rocks and stared up at the narrow path that ended high in a small black hole. A raven, which at first he mistook for a hawk, swooped in over the simmering blue behind the mountain and landed by the bushes and water of the oasis. It strutted cockily along the damp sand, unconcerned about Dirk. Hello, it said in a voice like a four year old.

At a nature reserve Dirk had once run into a talking crow. They kept it in a cage. He had thought a child was calling out to him as he looked at various exhibits. He finally realized it was the crow. Hello. Hello. A little girl wanting you to be her friend.

Dirk lowered his pack and squatted by the raven.

"Hello," he said.

Hello, hello, came the young child voice. The raven continued to stride up and down the sand, one eye glittering at Dirk.

"Who taught you how to talk, hey?" asked Dirk.

The raven snatched a bug out of the air, swallowed it, glanced at Dirk and called, Hello, hello. What's your story?

"What?"

Hello. What's your story?

Dirk sat down in the hot sand and smiled. The raven continued to strut.

"You really want my story, raven? I loved a God and gave away my life. And I loved a woman named Rachel and a little girl named Rebecca and this God that I loved took them away from me. So I came to America and I loved again. Sarah and my children, Bobby and Ginger. And then I did something, raven. I thought it was for the God I loved. I tried to create a good thing. People died. Sarah and Bobby and Ginger died. What did I do it for, raven? To make myself famous? To indulge my righteous anger and my passions? To put our church on the map and watch it grow? I thought the other churches would back us up but they didn't. Afraid of controversy. Afraid of losing members. Afraid of being threatened. And now I'm afraid, raven. Afraid I'm out of love. Afraid I don't believe in the God I threw my life away to thirty years ago. I'm all alone. This is the end of the line. There's no family to go back to when the holidays are over. No home. No church. My friends are awkward with me, they want to make it all better overnight. But it isn't that easy, is it, raven? I'm kind of far away right now. Far away from anything that ever mattered. Tried to be a Christian. Found out most of the people in the churches aren't interested in being that. They want something else. Maybe a big warm god they can put in a shrine in the corner of the room. Leave their Bible there. Light sticks of incense. Pull their Bible verse horoscope from the plastic loaf of bread. Make money. Sleep tight. No boats rocked. No risks taken. No love lost. No bonfires lit in the night. The night is for sleeping, not for light. No stars, raven, no stars. But either Christianity is an incarnation or it is nothing. Either it is flesh and bone and a heartbeat or I can't go back to it. Up to its neck in good and evil. Over its head in heaven and hell. All my lovers are dead. All the children I swore to protect. If spirit does not become flesh all of the love and the losing of love means nothing. It is just thin air. I won't go back to an abstraction. Is Jesus in us or is he just a concept that makes an institution prosper? What is it going to be, raven? Is Christianity the very stuff of life, in the thick of it, or does it exist in isolation? God help me, I love you, but I can't go back if it isn't life and death and right and wrong and black and white. I would rather travel in the desert until my bones bleach in the sun than go back to a place where the death of my son and my daughters is neither here nor there and of no consequence to the gospel of Jesus Christ. Either he bleeds and we bleed or it is nothing but a great farce. Raven, that's my story. Not much of an ending."

The raven caught another insect, flapped its wings vigorously and left. Dirk never saw it again. He never saw anything or anyone. He unrolled the sleeping bag Max had given him at the side of the pool. He slept and in the daytime he waited. Nothing happened. The desert stretched in every direction, his whole world, and he supposed it moved and lived and did what deserts ought to do, but all he saw was the sun and the blue sky and the purple sand. Only at night did he feel and hear the gentle quiet of a zephyr rushing close to the earth, hissing and sighing and soothing and crying, blowing the sand and breaking down the rocks and the plants and shifting them, shaping them, moving them along and slowly forming a new desert, a new world, a new heaven and a new earth.

CHAPTER 5

OREGON BEACHES

IT STRUCK HIM ON that particular afternoon by the sea that most of the Christians he had met in his life preferred illusion to truth. In fact, they equated faith with a fierce denial of reality: "I am feeling sad. But Christians are not supposed to feel sad. Therefore I cannot be sad. I must be happy." The suppression of what a person actually felt and the super-imposition of what a person thought ought to be felt was called an act of faith. The task of Christendom seemed to have become one of obscuring reality and replacing it with something much nicer, if less honest. Happiness for sadness, gentleness for rage, conviction and resoluteness for doubt. Christianity had become a mind game.

For faith was no longer a divine appointment that fortified you, and enabled you to face reality head on and go through it to the other side, and by so doing alter reality in actuality. Faith was now a denial of reality that enabled you to act as if what was so was not so, and to charge on ahead into an altered reality that existed only in your own mind and never in heaven or earth. Christianity had become more than a mind game then, even much more than an illusion. It had become the abuse of a substance, a narcotic, a hallucinogenic, a spiritual crack. How ferocious a Christian would become if someone sought to remove the veneer of abuse and thus expose the infrastructure of delusion: "But you are depressed, Erin. It is all right to say so. That doesn't mean you have no faith. Taking your depression to God is your faith, like the woman who brings her leprosy. Believing he will walk with you through the valley of the shadow of this death is your faith. The scriptures do not teach dishonesty."

They would fly at him all fang and claw and blazing zeal if he attempted to dissuade them from a forced cheerfulness, for this was their act of faith that God would make a reality, if only they forged that reality with their minds and refused to relinquish it. He was not allowed to prick the balloon, not permitted to question the sanctity of their imagined world. They would not look at the passages in scripture of those who struggled and agonized and stared reality in the face in the name of God and battled fiercely with it. No. The holy denial gave them peace. The fabrication was more real to them than reality itself, truer to them than truth. How many generations had this gone on, how powerful was the addiction?

Roman could not begin to guess. He simply knew that day on his vacation, as the combers rolled white and recreated the sand beach, smoothing all, removing all, leaving fragments of seashells, small dead crabs, and long ropes of kelp, that he could not teach at the seminary anymore, that he could not pastor at the church anymore. He could no longer be a dealer or a pusher. Not that he actively promoted the faith drug. But he was part of a system that did and by his presence he aided and abetted and gave credibility to what was destroying authentic Christianity. He could not return. Yet he did not wish to become a renegade and separate himself and live on locusts in the wilderness. Where would he go? And who would go with him?

This kind of thinking came with the mists of summer along the Oregon coast, mild grey clouds that blew off the Pacific and boiled past in the grasses and houses of the shoreline. They had rented a cabin for August and when his wife Brittany and their two young children were up to something else, Roman waded through the surf that peeled itself free of the ocean in long white strips. The roar of the breakers was constant, like a wind through tall mountain evergreens, but throatier, huskier. It blotted out all other sounds, obliterated useless and distracting thoughts. It laid a man bare. For Roman, the beach and the sea that could not cease from movement was the site of greatest honesty, a shrine.

On days of great wind and madness the waves thundered in with the white plumes of horses' heads, rearing in the blast and the storm. He let the phlegm and frenzy spatter him and chill him and he refused to flinch from the violent hooves of foam. Soon his own thoughts and prayers ran from him clear and sharp down to the sea. And some nights of foghorns and winking lights, with the sand smooth and taut as sheet metal, mirroring all, he removed his clothing and folded it neatly, and walked into the splintering water, and it pierced him, the cold punched through everything, stopped every thought, so that he often felt the most wonderful moments of his life were when he dove into water and hung suspended in the cool liquid with bubbles and the blue and green colours and the sense of belonging to nothing yet.

Some days came on in a great hurry of blue and limitless light and painfully bright unfurlings of sea and a white wind that sprouted kites of dawn and sunfall and twilight. Then it was that he knelt in the sand with his children and built great and wondrous castles with moats and driftwood drawbridges and tunnels and high towers resplendent with gull feathers, then it was that Suzanne and Tristan bought a delta kite and a diamond kite from a shop full of kites, full of space and colour and fresh breezes that caused everything in the shop to flutter or fly or chime or peal like the shining bells of a grand old church, and into the sky he went with them, in air that was a festival, a thousand worlds' colours and shapes flicking and darting and swooning and curling, and they with their dolphins springing over the sun, all of them drawn up into the heavens, as if they were diving far up into a sea that was an arch, falling up like feathers into it, rising like the long looping strings of the kites, caught up to zephyrs and mare's tails and daylight's half moons and the summer's blue of a nine year old's mind that ripples like a crimson kite, taut and humming and tumbling on its line, a sailfish snared and plunging in sea and out of sea, the drops from every snap of the tail a startling and predestined constellation.

Somehow it was decided and with remarkably little conflict. Brittany had impulsively waded into the tumult of the incoming tide in an expensive black evening gown and, watching the loose dark silk swirling like a school of slick, sliding fish, she wrinkled up her nose and its freckles like a finger and said, "If you spend a year writing a book, I want to nurse in Mexico for a year. Deal?"

The sun slipped into her wind bush of hair and burned there. She was looking at him but the fire was behind her so her face and eyes were black. She often smiled when he thought she should be angry.

"All that Master's degree ever did was lock me into a desk and paperwork. I want to hold a kid's hand again. I want to bring some life back into the world."

He shrugged. "Of course."

She came out of the water shining and placed her slender arms around his neck and kissed him a long time. Tristan and Suzanne hooted and raced along the flaming beach to get away, disappearing into the brilliance as if into a shimmering palace of great magic. Roman and Brittany laughed and held on and the gown stuck to his pant legs, soaking and chilling him, but it was all very good, and salt and sand were wonderful in her hair.

They rented a cabin on a cliff for the year, the wood stove keeping out the raw Pacific winter, the rolling storms and the sleet. Brittany home schooled the children at the kitchen table while Roman wrote at a small desk in their bedroom, his knees cramped, their voices honest gifts of God that did not disturb but assured him that he dwelt and scribbled in safety.

He wrote seven essays that winter. It seemed the words had been crammed and crowded and jammed to bursting, and once he meant business and finally put mind and pen to paper, they boiled up and out, making great dark streaks over the white. In the first essay he compared the lust for warehouse shopping with the lust for warehouse churches, big, bigger, biggest, and the dazzle, the vanity fair of it, the chilling anonymity of it, the herding, the grey crowd-think, the passive-aggressive Sunday mob. In the second he discussed the Christian drive for the instant and the effortless in the spiritual life, indeed in every facet of the Christian's life, no doubt an absorption of the luxury cult of North America, but even more sinister when God's Spirit was reduced to a time-saving device, a kind of divine food processor that whipped, blended and smoothed out all. The third essay was about the Church's preoccupation with what was sensual and experiential over against what was intellectual and reflected. Feel-good Christianity was superior to think-well Christianity in the majority of believers' minds, as mutually exclusive as oil and water, and a good thing too, they thought, for what did Pentecost have to do with Oxford, who needed brain when you had spirit?

Then there was the corollary essay on the dramatic and the sensational, hype, hyper, hypest, a grand bazaar of spiritual special effects, every worship and ministry time more extravagant than the week before, a Church addicted to melodrama, addicted to megalomania, thrashing and dying in a melanoma of the skin-deep that had metastasized to the soul. This was followed by a piece on the worship of the present, the indifference to the past when God had done very little comparatively, and the denial of the future which simply would not be since the world must end long before 2050, and all that could be must now be, and the present, our present, was the grand age of the ages, ours was the chosen generation, nothing had fully existed before us or could after us, the now, the now, the god of now. His sixth essay considered sound and silence, or better, sound versus silence, for the Church would be silent no more, She would shout it from the rooftops. Where was God in the long silences where one man coughed? Give us voices, give us a band, an orchestra, give us volume, the joyful noise, the rising crescendo. Obliterate us, oh God, in the ringing and singing and banging and blasting, we want to feel and absorb and become sound. Do not leave us in a silence where dark discovery may lay, where an angel's emerald eye may pin us, where you, oh God, may whisper and we may catch it, catch you, catch all. We do not know our way in the silence. Have pity and drown us in a Noahic deluge of roar.

Before he wrote the final essay, Roman unpacked a tenor saxophone that gleamed like old Spanish gold. He had not played it in twenty years. At first it squawked and he got his spit wrong. But then it began to tie the stars together in clusters and he took the narrow path down the cliffside to play barefoot in the breakers, his trousers rolled up to his thighs, keeping back the bone-cracking cold with his lips, playing and swaying and stirring stars into great swirls of singing light, hair whirling in a wind, nights of moon also coming for their say, plating black night and old sax with hot silver that cooled to the touch, sound on sound on sound, and then silence, so that the surf could have its way, gurgling and gushing and grating and rushing, to where only sand and weed, whale and sea horse and sailfish could play.

And then he stuffed his legs under the small pinewood desk and wrote the seventh essay. He argued for a return to depth and quiet, to song that meadowlarked and whipoorwilled, to metaphor and similie and soliloquy, to a swing of psalms and a galloping light of gospels and epistles, of a genesis, and the long slanting beams of exodus. Make music, he wrote, string your thoughts like water beads on kite thread, and let the line in your hands shiver in winds you are unafraid to call mysteries. Explain what you can, yet admit to your gibberish before God, lisp and bubble and cry in confession.

But paint, by all means paint, let your theology bear the rugged gouge of the palette knife, let your oils be thick and lustrous and layered, layer upon layer down to a bare canvas heart stretched to wood. Let your spirituality be in thick strokes too, or if you grow weak, fine lines of light, trace them and interlace them, string and fling and rise like a bird on the wing, speak of what is true and let them say you flew in honesty like a sky.

But do it all in beauty, let your syllables be lovely, and your pauses, speak what God speaks, ride his language if you can, stride on his couplet, but come back to the small, the little brood on the beach for whom Christ is cutting and cleaning fish, take your sustenance there, and for the crowd that gathers and swarms for a show, don't go, don't go there, where you can know every face, stay and listen and grow. Hold the shine of God's oceans in your hand, and thank Christ, and bless the God and Father in every glint and gleam, and do not waste one day's heaven in folly.

When Roman read over his manuscript, often speaking it out loud to Brittany, he saw water and wave and sea star and often sensed the hiss and white feather of the sounding grey whale.

"There is too much ocean," he groaned.

Brittany shook her head. She scowled with her own lines of wind and water and frost dawns under the long and longing curve of the storm-swooping gulls. "God's ocean."

"The language is like a poet's. It's no good. No one will take it seriously. No one will read it."

"They read the psalms."

"I am a professor. And a pastor. I can't hold all this in my head. A dead Church and all these dancing words? No one holds those together and lives through it."

"You've put it down. You don't have to hold it. Ro, you're in good company. Hopkins was a priest. Donne and Bunyan and MacDonald were pastors. Lewis was the professor who scrawled poems and stories. That's a grand gathering at the old hearth, don't you think?"

"No one will publish it."

"Oh. Were you thinking of a lot of money?"

They both laughed. She was at the kitchen table while he stood, and her chin was on her palm, her hair unwinding winding flame in a sun-square window, and her eyes winked a delicate filigree green.

"What will you call it?"

"SHORELINE: Seven essays where heaven meets earth. Something like that."

Nose and freckles wrinkled.

"Okay," he smiled. "What then?"

She got up and stretched, her Aran sweater bunching at her shoulders. Hands on her hips, she looked out the window and down the cliff to the sand where their children had made a fort of precariously balanced driftwood.

"OREGON BEACHES," she said and turned to him, grinning, pushing back her bangs with her ring hand. "Seven essays for pilgrims on the shore. Something like that."

In the end she got the title, he settled for a subtitle. He called it ORE-GON BEACHES, *essays on the shore between the Church and the Divine.* He mailed it to three different publishing houses one day and then went back to bed and did not dream. Spring was lighting on the sea and every morning he went down to the beach to watch. In four months they would be in Mexico City, a very different place, and he did not think he felt any better than he had before he sourced the coursing tributary from his mind. He ought to be more at peace. After all, he had articulated the ache and the rage in his heart. But within was an opaque sky where no gulls flew, no diving ospreys exhilarated. He left footprints, the sea took them, and he left them again.

At Christmas they had found a small church, a hole in the wall called Champion's Cross. The pastor wore white robes and had a speech imped-iment, his words coming out slowly and with a great many pauses. It was a quiet place, the singing soft, the scripture reading like dreams, but Roman always came back every Sunday evening to go gently with them into the presence of the divine where there was much that he had forgot-ten and much that he had never taken to heart. There were thirty or forty of them and he got to know them all, and the pastor too, who spoke clear-ly and concisely when he was not preaching, using the finely groomed words of an academic. Champion's Cross used a liturgy obviously fash-ioned from several others, woven like a basket of willow and reeds, and it was a warm thing, it lilted like a fine piece of jazz, and he took it to the beach with his tenor sax and played, a head of words and the notes oblig-ing them in the clear night air, and it went on and long and phosphores-cence struck when the sea rose happily to his chest. Once or twice he scarcely had his footing. But it was always the right thing to do, to wor-ship at Champion's Cross, to listen to the halting sentence and the God of the pauses, to wind his sax into the carnation-red sun, like the night's bou-tonniere, and the rose-white burn of the evening star, heaven's torch and the harbinger of a thousand lights, over his head like crystal, a fine, fine dusting of snow that never lit on him but showered the high heavens, falling up and out forever. Play on, he urged, play on, though the tide was practically lifting him and fish slipped between his legs and nibbled at his toes, God, God, hear my voice, hear heart and soul and mind and strength, take it all and twist it about the tight ornament of infinity. So the moon always found him, that tide swayer, blowing the sax towards the far meadows of gone light, at the dark layered on dark, noir en noir, the tourists strolling by with running shoes in their hands, laughing at this clown of the Oregon beaches, but a few stopped to listen, just as he listened at Champion's Cross, and he played and worshipped until his fingers could no longer move with the night.

A few weeks before Mexico Brittany came home with the mail. She looked at Roman steadily, her green eyes broad and expansive and light-pitted as a calming sea. The mail was in a plastic bag in her hand.

"Ro, was it a good year?"

"What?"

"Was the writing fine enough, and Champion's Cross, and having us?"

"What are you talking about?"

"Just answer me. Was it a good year? You came at it all crunched up into a ball."

"I wrote what I wanted to write. There was a church at Champion's Cross. I hadn't played my sax since I was a student. I needed the year like I need great breaths of air."

She emptied the bag at the kitchen table where he sat with a newspaper and a tea. There was a pile of white and brown envelopes of various sizes, as well as a long tube. She sorted out one large manila envelope and dropped it in front of him. The return address was for a publishing firm so that meant it was his manuscript. A stab inside and he looked up at her. She held another large and bulky manila envelope and dropped it on top of the other. He pushed back his chair.

"I'm down to the beach." He pulled on a sweater. The July afternoon had cooled to a tight breeze that pricked whitecaps.

"What about your sax?"

"No."

He moved past her, eyes already on the long water, when she grasped his arm.

"You just told me it was a good year."

"So?"

"You didn't mention publishing, Ro. You did care, I know, but it was a big enough year without that, wasn't it?"

"Sure. Talking to myself. Playing to myself."

"You wanted an audience?"

"Doesn't everyone?"

"It was you and God, wasn't it? That's all you had, wailing away at that thing and begging the sea to drown you. You just told me it was a good year."

"All right. It was and it wasn't. Let me go down."

"What more did you need, Ro?"

"You take in, you give out, isn't that the way it's supposed to work? Isn't that how you breathe? I stuttered my piece like old Bruce at Champion's Cross. But I didn't have thirty, I didn't even have ten. What's the point, Britt? Just me and my shadow?"

She crossed her arms and sat on the edge of the table. "I'm sorry to hear you say that."

"Yeah, me too, I'm sorry too."

"Wait."

"Let me go, will you, Britt? What is it now? Another pep talk?"

"No."

She had tucked a white envelope under her teal sweatshirt and into the waistband of her jeans and she was pulling it out and holding it towards him.

"What?"

"Well, look at it."

He took it. She had already opened it. Just a thin envelope with one sheet of typed paper. He caught the return address. He looked at her and she was laughing.

"Yes, Ro." She clapped her hands. "And what will you do with your great audience? One book won't be enough, will it?"

"Are you serious?"

"Read it."

"No, I'll take it down to the beach."

"Fine, take it down to the beach, but don't let the wind snap it out of your hand. You'll want to frame it."

She punched him on the arm hard. He caught her up and dragged her down the path with him and all the time she shouted about supper. He tossed her into the sea. Tristan and Suzanne came tearing out of the driftwood fort, yelling, "We'll help you, Mom," and the three of them pinned him to the sand before Brittany hunted up a mop of fresh seaweed to scrub his face.

That Sunday the four of them were at Champion's Cross. The white plaster continued to fade to yellow, the singing was no more than a whisper, there was a quarter hour of silent prayer, Bruce the pastor limped through his message, and Roman felt a surge of glory.

"Is the Church dead?" Brittany asked as they went barefoot at the edge of the surf Monday morning. "Are you dead?"

"I can't say that I am."

"The fine thing about death is resurrection."

"There's lots that is no good out there, Britt. Beaches and books and Champion's Cross can't make all the ugliness disappear."

"They mean you can choose."

"Yes. There's nothing like being able to breathe."

Suddenly Roman laughed up at a sky no different than the sea below it, blue and white and moving quickly, and he laughed at all the worlds that had no words, and he thought of playing his saxophone to a Mexican child, to a dozen of them or a hundred of them or to one of them, and he imagined how the dust must swing in all that light like angels dancing on the head of a pin.

CHAPTER

ST. NATE'S-AMONG-THE-FOOLS

IT WAS NOT A bar. It was never that. Johnny had been an alcoholic up until he was 46 and he had no intention of going back to the seventh level of hell. You could get coffee, you could get tea, cappuccinos and mochas and expressos and hot almond milk, you could get good food, especially Chinese food, you might get a corned beef or pastrami or smoked salmon sandwich, hefty ones when the band was live, and you could get the salmon with Winnipeg cream cheese if you asked. You couldn't smoke, not even in the john. It interfered with the jazz. How could you get your piano (your no) right, your trumpet (your horn), your bone (your trombone), or your sax, with billows of burning tobacco stinging your eyes? Sweet, clean, and tight at Johnny O's. If you had to have the vices there were other places to go.

The trouble was, Johnny O's had the attitude, the personality, it had a gal named Cassandra, and it had the bands—16th Street Baptist Church, Alchemy, Godchild, and Slang. And if it was the daylight hours and the bands weren't playing, it had the hottest tracks—Count Basie, Duke Ellington, Miles Davis, Johnny Coltrane, the Dave Brubeck Quartet, Louis Armstrong, Dizzy Gillepsie, George Benson, the Branford Marsalis Trio. But no videos. If the band wasn't live you just used your ears and drank coffee.

Johnny O's was a class act. Everybody went there around the time the century was fading and the new thousand years breaking loose. Students. Lawyers. Doctors. Priests. Poets. Professors. It was only a few blocks from the campus gates so the student crowd dominated during the wet and slick winter, but the others took their own back in spring and summer.

Johnny became fast friends with one person in particular, a professor long and thin as an oboe, who wore tweed and Clark Kent glasses and a narrow, tightly-knotted tie. He taught divinity and seemed an unlikely candidate for a jazz coffeehouse. His hair did not even flow past his shirt collar in renegade scholar style. But his fingers were strong and long and tapered and once, when only Johnny and Cassandra were there, he sat down and made the shining black Steinway dance. He knew his music and you got the impression there were no CDs at home, no cassettes, just vinyl, immaculately kept and glinting like a rainy night, with no pops or crackles as the needle slid precisely over the grooves. His name was Gypp, Dr. Winston Gypp. His wife's name, a nickname which Gypp always used, rhymed with his own name. Slip, he called her. Her other name, the one nobody remembered, was Irene.

As Johnny and Gypp became close friends they exchanged music and stories and books. Johnny had dozens of bios on the jazz masters, as well as other books on steam locomotives, which the two of them shared a passion for. They planned a trip to India, where the proud locomotives still ran, and went over and over the details for years. Gypp would spread out snapshots of locomotives at the front coffee bar as if he and Johnny were playing some sort of double solitaire. They would pick them up, put them down, adjust their sequence, create patterns rectangular and circular, shuffle them into separate piles. Gypp lent Johnny some classic vinyls, the slip covers looking as if he had just purchased the albums, yet the majority had been released in the 40's and 50's. After a year and a bit, Gypp began to bring Johnny books too. Not jazz or locomotive books. Theology books.

"This is your namesake," he told Johnny in a Gloucestershire accent as soft as a smooth sax. "I think you can probably get a good deal out of that."

Johnny turned the green-bound book over to glance at the gold lettering stamped on the spine. "John Owen," he read. "Are you kidding me?"

"No, I am not. Anyone who loves jazz and steam must not only be a deep man, a soul man, if you will, but a man close to both heaven and earth."

"I've never read this kind of stuff, Gypp. Really."

"Well, Johnny, this is a good time for you to start. You have the perfect environment—coffee, jazz, and bright spirits. It is true you may find the first piece a bit of rough going. But you will master it. The language has a swing all its own. It is happily addictive."

"Okay, Gypp, I'll give it a try. Coffee?"

"Not this evening, I think. A glass of almond milk, please."

"At your table?"

"Yes, please. Is there any lemon chicken left?"

"Cassandra saved you some."

"Ah, Cassandra, thank you."

Cassandra grinned, tall and strong and full of light, hair a long swing of sax and no. "You're always on our minds, Gypp."

"Well. That is a good place to be."

As the friendship ripened, like no and trombone playing off each other, Gypp would come in and call, "Good evening, Johnny Owen."

"'Lo, Gypp. You drop by for Trillium?"

"Are they playing? I had a class until ten this evening and they asked rather enormous questions. I came to unwind. Slip will be joining me."

"We're pretty packed."

"Yes, I see that. Well, Johnny, do you have a table for me or shall I go home and make good use of my gramophone?"

"We always have a table for you," Cassandra would toss over her shoulder. She'd play with the cappuccino machine so that it hissed and roared as if it were about to blow up. Then she'd find the card table behind the front bar and set it up with plush captain's chairs.

"So, Gypp?" she'd smile. "Lemon chicken?"

"Chow mein, I think. And one of your sandwiches. Montreal corned beef. On sourdough rye. You do have some of the bread left, don't you?"

"Always. Something to drink?"

"Yes, please. A tea. Prince of Wales."

"You're the only one who ever asks for that."

"Well. I expect I am the only one who has been to Caernarfon."

"What's that?"

"It is the castle in Wales where the Prince is investitured, a custom dating back to 1284 and Edward I."

"Sometime you and Slip will have to take me travelling. You'd be better than a Fodor's."

"Just tell us when, Cassandra. I think you would make a wonderful travelling companion."

Gypp dropped in one winter's afternoon when the streets and the sky were the same colour. Johnny grabbed a dark French roast and joined him at a table while Charlie Parker went in and out and all around them.

"Gypp. Did Johnny Owen really write this stuff in English? Or is this a translation or something?"

"Why?"

"I don't know. It can be stiff."

"Well, Johnny Owen, our Johnny Owen in fact wrote everything in Latin first, then he translated it into English. That's very astute of you."

"I could feel it. The words didn't have enough play. Sure, there's a lilt, like you said, but it's like a band that's always warming up. I don't mean what he says. I mean how he says it."

Gypp sipped his hot almond milk and bit into a lightly buttered croissant. "Did Cassandra make these?"

"Yeah. She used our big oven in the back."

"They are wonderful. You should marry that girl, Johnny."

"Sure. I'm a real catch at 48."

"Don't you have a lot in common?"

"What? Jazz and coffee?"

"That's better than most. You should ask the girl out."

"Are you serious?"

"Yes."

"She's taller than me."

"So am I. But we get along well."

"She's beautiful. I'm her boss. She's always up. My moods are muddled."

"Do you know any other languages?"

"What do you want me to do? Serenade her in French or Italian?"

"I meant, are you good at languages?"

"I've never tried."

"Try Latin."

"What?"

"You told me you wanted to hear Johnny Owen hot, didn't you?"

"But I can't learn Latin."

"Why not?"

"It's old stuff."

"So is Charlie Parker. But I see your foot tapping."

"I don't have any books."

"I do. Cambridge University Press has published a very good set. Shall I drop them off?"

"Are you trying to convert me or something, Gypp?"

"Well, I can't do anything like that, Johnny. That's between you and God. I'm just the middleman."

"What's the big deal?"

"The big deal, Johnny, is that God is like jazz. And if you love jazz, which you do, it means you two already have a lot in common."

"How do you figure that?"

"Well, doesn't jazz pick you up and take you outside of yourself?"

"Sometimes."

"Good. Well, sometimes we experience God as transcendent. He is wonderful and awesome and quite outside of us."

"Is that all?"

"No, it is not. Sometimes the jazz is right in you, your heart, your lungs, your mind, your whole body. It can be quite visceral, Johnny, can it not? Yes, well, God is like that too. Going right through you, and in and out and around, like a good solo. He can make your whole being resonate. Body and soul, Johnny. Transcendent and immanent. As jazz, so is God. Or better, as God, so is jazz."

"You blow me away, Gypp. God is a sax solo by Johnny Coltrane?"

"Why not? That's as good a metaphor as any. Though I should prefer to put it that Johnny Coltrane was a sax solo by God."

"Is this what you talk like in your classroom?"

"Ah, well. The classroom is many things, Johnny. But it is not Fats Waller and it is not Johnny O's. You must suit your language to your audience. Which," he said, rising and patting Johnny's shoulder, "is why Latin will make you swing. Are you game?"

Johnny laughed in a great burst of sound. Cassandra was leaning against the bar and watching them. When Johnny laughed, she laughed too, all of her, and shook her head. Then she started clearing tables, swooping up cups and saucers and plates, brushing crumbs, in a sudden hurry of energy.

Gypp pronounced Johnny a genius at Latin and in less than a year he was reading not only passages of Johnny Owen, but of Augustine and Thomas Aquinas too. About this time Cassandra bought Johnny a book Gypp had authored for a Christmas present. When Gypp and Slip showed up for the New Year's bash, Johnny came over with the book for Gypp to sign while one musician thrashed at his no and another spilt light out of his trumpet.

"I'm disappointed it's not in Latin."

"Well, Johnny, I speak to the times."

"You never told me you wrote. How many other books do you have out there?"

"A lot."

"Are they any good?"

"You love all your books just as you love all your children. I am not ashamed of them and each one has its own strong points."

"Do they swing?"

"Let's hope so, Johnny. I'm afraid I'm not the one to ask. They are on my shelf, and I thank God I have been able to write them, but I rarely look at my published books. There is a great deal I should like to write and I have to get on with that."

"I'm working through two of Johnny Owen's pieces but I'm going to lay them aside and dig right into yours. Then we're going to go over what you write, not just what the dead guys are talking up."

"I'm game, Johnny, but I'd rather you finished Johnny O first. What are you reading?"

"A lot of interesting stuff about fiat lux and getting up close and personal with God."

"Animadversions on 'Fiat Lux'? On Communion with God?"

"Those are the ones, Gypp."

"Finish them, please. Then we can talk about my book."

Gypp and Slip stayed until the coffeehouse closed at three. The four of them sat in a dimness that smelt of sweat and ground coffee beans while the cappuccino machine gleamed silent behind the bar. Slip was the tiniest of them all but burst frequently with laughter and fight and mischief, eyes flashing with the rainlight from the street. Gypp's hair was white and short and neatly combed and had been that way since he was fifty, but Slip's was a brash red that she would not surrender to God or man. It lit her whole body. Gypp would laugh with heart at her tangy expressions, and once that very long night and early morning called her his "Welsh rarebit". Cassandra took to her spark and flame and they made plans for a late lunch the next day, which they followed through on while Gypp and Johnny remained in their beds and slept.

That entire year was taken up with Gypp's books. There were fifteen and Johnny read them all, one after the other, like a chain smoker, scarcely finishing one before he picked up the next. At Johnny O's Gypp and Johnny talked about life and death, and heaven and hell, and God and man and beast. Behind them and over them soared the saxes and the bones and in their skin and in their blood thumped the drums, while at the back of all their thinking and questioning and debating and wondering, the no, up and down, under and over, on and on. It was Tempest or Inferno or Breezes, it was Armstrong or Basie or Ellington, it was the Brecker Brothers or Billie Holiday or Herbie Hancock or Lena Horne, it was Thelonious Monk or Sonny Rollins or Chet Baker.

Gypp leaned back and smiled slyly and patted his stomach after one invigorating evening with Johnny. He pronounced the discussion as good as a feast, splendid as a Yorkshire pudding by the side of a well-cooked beef Wellington, with plenty of rich gravy and a cool wedge of Stilton cheese, followed up by a steaming pot of Prince of Wales. A young woman named Dusky Shrove swept the room with gales of darkness and light, pricks of sweat on her arms and face like precise constellations in a spring twilight, and Gypp let himself go, eyes closed, unsmiling, swaying slightly with the rhythms and the throaty voice and the swirling sax. The song went on for twenty minutes and Gypp went with it as far as he could go, swinging from side to side almost imperceptibly. When the music ended and the coffeehouse erupted in applause and whistles, Gypp became still but he did not open his eyes.

"You look like you're praying."

"A cathedral is a fine place for prayer, Johnny Owen. But I'm certain the world is your cathedral when you worship. It doesn't matter if it is a Calcutta slum or a hut in the Alps or Windsor Castle. If you are there and there is prayer then God is there. Even at Johnny O's."

Dusky Shrove began to sing softly into the mike and the sax went with her like a warm shadow, taking shape, giving her added length and substance, balancing and extending and anchoring, and Gypp went along with her too, eyes shut, a gentle swaying, tie knotted to his throat, tweed jacket hung over the back of his chair, white shirt with a ballpoint clipped to its breast pocket luminous in the dark and in the spots of yellow light. Both pale hands were on the table. The left one began to pat the beat. Otherwise Gypp was not there.

Johnny began to date Cassandra. He told Gypp the first time she'd held him when they went dancing he'd felt like a teenager who had rockets blasting through him and out the top of his head. As November rains gusted off the north Pacific, Johnny and Cassandra asked Gypp to marry them on Christmas Eve since he was an ordained Anglican priest. Gypp agreed and at six o'clock on December 24th, two hundred people crammed into Johnny O's where Gypp performed the marriage ceremony on the bandstand. It was from the old Book of Common Prayer written by Thomas Cranmer, with a few additions from the Song of Solomon and the Psalms. Part of the ceremony was in English and the rest of it was in Latin. Once Johnny had kissed the bride and their friends and patrons were cheering, Dusky Shrove launched into Amazing Grace accompanied by sax and horn. Everyone enjoyed fresh coffee and croissants and then the whole crowd followed Johnny and Cassandra and Gypp and Slip to St. Nathaniel's-among-the-schools for a midnight Eucharist. The church got its name from the time the university had all its colleges in the neighbourhood. Some went forward and knelt but most only watched and bawled the carols with a Johnny O's gusto. Dusky overpowered them all and had the rector peering up from his liturgy every time she danced off with the words of one of the Christian hymns. A rare snowfall was tiptoeing over the city when they emerged from St. Nathaniel's. Johnny and Cassandra headed for the airport and a red-eye flight to New Orleans. The others went home to bed. Gypp sat awake, drumming his fingers on the quilt while Slip buried herself under the covers and disappeared.

Just before Easter, with cherry blossoms twirling up and over the greening lawns, Gypp, who had made himself scarce, dropped by for an evening of jazz with Dusky Grove and Godchild. The entire room was smoothed over with the brown liquid sounds. Cassandra waved and turned back to her crashing cappuccino machine. Johnny came over and sat. They shook hands.

"So?"

"How are you, Johnny?"

"It's been a good week. Hey, it's been a good year. I should've got married when I was fifteen."

"How is the condo?"

"Fine. Cassan's got plants everywhere. There's even a lipstick plant right over our bed. I keep dreaming it's going to fall down on top of us one night."

"Any thoughts on family?"

"What? After four months? Easy goes, Gypp. What about you? Written any new books?"

"Well, that's just it, Johnny, no, I haven't, and it worries me."

"Why? It's not as if you haven't published anything."

"The other books are well and good. But there is something I want to say and I haven't said it. When I'm sitting here, it comes to me. But when I return to my study, it vanishes."

"Maybe I need to set up a study for you here."

"I've thought about that. But how would it work? If our friends kept dropping by for a chat I wouldn't get any writing done."

"That's easy. I stick you off by yourself, even rig up a screen or something, and Cassan and I would chase everyone away. They'd never know you were there half the time anyway. Come in the back door."

"Are you sure about this, Johnny?"

"Absolutely. Can't think of anyplace I'd rather have you than right here."

"I'll think on it. Barth used to play Mozart and snort on his pipe while he wrote his Dogmatics. Count Basie would do for me. Or Dusky Shrove and Godchild."

"Let me know."

"I've decided. I should like to begin right now. Over in that corner, I think. You can find a screen later if you wish. I have my papers here in my briefcase. A cup of dark French roast would do nicely. A pot of it, if that's not too much trouble. And a sandwich. Pastrami. Yes, that would be enough to start. Keep Dusky singing, would you?"

"I'll tell her she's helping to create a masterpiece."

"Well, Johnny, I have no idea what it will be but D.O.M. will apply here, I assure you. Deo gloria maximo."

"To God. The best. The greatest?"

"Very good. Perhaps you will surpass your namesake and give us a systematic theology, something that will explain earth, wind, fire, and angels, the whole thing."

"I'd love to write a book and do that. The trouble is, I don't have all the answers myself. I'm not sure how much I believe of what I read."

"Yes, well, that's between you and God, Johnny Owen. I just watch and pray. And sometimes argue."

"What is this thing you have to write about?"

"God becoming flesh. Yes, I know, I've mentioned it in my other writings. But I've never done one book just on that. And it's everything, Johnny. It's the whole matter, the summa theologica. It's where the transcendent God is visceral. Quite frankly, the thought of setting anything remotely appropriate about it down on paper is unnerving. But I have to try. Tell Dusky to put all her soul into it and perhaps I won't make a hash of it. And now, Johnny, I must run."

So they moved an old scarred round wooden table into the corner and Gypp set up shop. Cassandra found a screen in a closet dotted with colourful posters of jazz greats. Gypp was delighted with this, of course, and once Cassandra put plants around the screen it looked as if it were a natural part of Johnny O's decor. Behind it, Gypp could see the band while he wrote in a dazzling flash of track lighting that Johnny had readjusted. The table was shortly littered with sheets of white paper, some blank, some with a few notations, others dense with small, precise scribble. Three nights a week Gypp did this while the bands blared and soothed, pausing only to sip Prince of Wales tea or dark French roast or hot almond milk or to use the washroom. No one noticed him. You could see him writing through the window from the street. But poets always hung around coffee houses, so why not?

Sometimes Slip joined Gypp at Johnny O's for a relaxing evening together and the music would get into Gypp's blood. He would kiss her and head over to his table behind the screen. After awhile Cassandra would drive Slip home, the pair tossing up shouts of laughter. Gypp would peel off his tweed jacket and work in his shirtsleeves until Johnny O's closed and then drive himself home in a luscious summer dark, his windows rolled down, and the honeysuckle breeze would muss his hair and play with his tie until he unknotted it.

Gypp might start a night's work on the book at what Johnny's patrons, ever since Christmas, called St. Nate's-among-the-fools, where he would sit in the burning bars of sunfall or, if it was later, the cooling black and the creaking and settling of old stone and wood. He closed his eyes and prayed and swayed lightly from side to side. Then he would go down to Johnny O's for the rest of the night.

The book took longer than he thought it might. Summer blew into the fresh rains of fall and winter and the roads shimmered under his feet. He began to come on Saturdays if he could steal away. November was Oscar Peterson month. Johnny played his tracks again and again and the songs mixed with God and worked their way through the small bones of Gypp's writing hand. Peterson was in the city that month but Gypp had missed out on the ticket sales. One evening he walked down from St. Nate's to Johnny O's and it was jammed, far beyond what it ought to have been on a Tuesday. He came through the back door and heard the ripple and roll

from Johnny's Steinway, polished to a blaze, and saw a heavy man hard
at work, bent over the jumping keys, going in and out of the crashing and
tumbling and chiming, in and out of the night and a blistering light,
through, through, and through, and the cataract broke over Gypp's head
and he closed his eyes a moment, then made his way to his table, unoccu-
pied behind the screen, and wrote while the no shook and trembled and
keened with pleasure. The words jostled and jumbled and bolted onto the
page, sheet after sheet, and the no sang to the cold winter rain that
hummed on the glass.

When the crowds had gone Johnny and Cassandra and the piano play-
er came and sat down with Gypp, who was leaning back in his chair with
his hands behind his head. He was delighted, nodding and laughing and
chatting in long, swift sentences with the jazz pianist, who put up his feet
and had a second almond milk and roared and threw up his hands and
enjoyed himself enormously. He had known Johnny Owen since the '60s
and all his vinyl and CDs that Johnny owned he had lavishley auto-
graphed. Gypp unpinned one of the posters from his screen that had long
ago promoted *Night Train* and the burly pianist swept a pen across it.
When it was time to leave Gypp rolled the poster carefully and tucked it
up the sleeve of his grey London Fog.

The next morning Gypp woke to a dreamy, sunny, bluey day, and had
a slow breakfast with Slip that was as cheerful as sun on the sea. He decided to drive past the ocean on his way to the university and gaze at the long
shining. When the rare Saturday make-up session was done he went down
to Johnny O's and parked. It was five o'clock and already filling up.
Dusky Shrove and a friend, Sassy Usher, were singing together tonight
backed by a new band, Blue's Blue And Silk. Gypp thumped up the road
and down a side-street to St. Nate's. Eucharist was celebrated at six and
after that he remained alone. As it grew dark he thought of the night
before, of the book, of the Incarnation, and lines from an ancient Irish
monk's poem tripped across his prayers, *I get wisdom day and night, turning darkness into light.*

Johnny found him there. He sat behind Gypp in the pews.

"Hello, Johnny. How are you?"

"You left all your papers at the O last night. Thought you might
be worried."

He produced a sheaf of papers black with writing. Gypp blinked
at them.

"Did I leave them there? I thought they were in my briefcase in the car."

"I read them."

"What? All of them?"

"I haven't been to bed."

"Well, Johnny. They must seem a kind of madness to you."

"St. Nate's-among-the-fools."

"Yes. Something like that. Kierkegaard said there was no way to rationalize it. A God-Man was a logical impossibility. All you could do was take a leap of faith. You couldn't reason it out. I am not entirely of his opinion. But I understand him. To a degree, he is right. In this world, only a fool would worship Christ. It makes no earthly sense. The human brain, on its own, cannot get itself around a God-Man.

"I am for the human brain, I am for precise formulation. God himself is not ambiguous. But the arguments can only take you so far. If heart and soul are not involved, there is no orthodoxy. If there is no love for God, no love for his people, no love for the commonwealth of his creation, there is no orthodoxy. If there is no passion, there is no orthodoxy.

"I told you it was like jazz, Johnny. If it grips you, it's jazz. If it doesn't, it's not the genuine article. If your brain alone is your theology, it's not theology. But if God grips you, well, then you will see Christ, you will see the God-Man. If God grips you, you have a theology that lives and breathes, heart, mind, soul, strength. When you have the Christ of the scriptures beating in your blood and brain, it's jazz.

"But if he does not seize you, if your heart does not warm, precise formulation establishes nothing and saves no one. It's just notes hammered out on the piano. There must be a *fiat lux*. Then it is possible to see and believe in the God-Man. Then to the whole world you will indeed be a fool. But a lucky fool."

Johnny set the papers on the pew next to where Gypp sat. Then he stood up and went to the front of the sanctuary. There was a click and a pool of light at a piano. Johnny hit four or five keys, toyed with a melody, then sat down. His fingers began to explore. Bright and bright and higher and higher. He lost himself. Gypp finally walked up to a piano on the other side, flicked on its light, and began to move up and out and in, rolling and rhyming and reaching, racing, twisting in and out of Johnny O's sound and searching, now off on his own, now back to weave and interweave and fashion a cradle for the Son of God. They scaled ladders to the heavens and toppled ringing to earth and rumbled back and forth between Gethsemane and Eden, between Bethlehem and Golgotha, between stables and gardens and cemeteries and hilltops. They did not look up at each other but they listened and went on and on together. Soon enough they fell into soft, spare ways, into twilights, into vespers and complines, into hushes and flowings, while car headlights cascaded over and over their heads, and so they dropped to whispers before the great star rose up and fired the earth. They turned off their lamps and remained seated at their benches.

"Quo?" asked Gypp.

"Christus," replied Johnny.

Johnny Owen and Cassandra were baptized that Christmas Eve at St. Nate's and confirmed, joining the Anglican communion. The rector permitted Dr. Winston Gypp to assist him in the rite.

Gypp's book on the Incarnation was completed and published. He considered it his apogee, though he would go on to write six or seven other works. A British reviewer commented: "The same balance and maturity is here, the same clarity and logical progression, but there seems a rather livelier note than that to which we are used to from Dr. Gypp, as if something had set the wind chimes to dancing. I offer no argument against his cogent and appealing debate for the deity of Christ. There remains a good deal of old Johnny Owen here, a spot of Lewis, a solid touch of a rather freeish Scottish reformed theology, the rounder, riper substantive sort you will find at St. Andrews or Aberdeen or Edinburgh, and finally a stroke of Barth at his best. There is such movement to-and-fro one wonders if Gypp too has not taken to writing his theology under the influence of Mozart. I know not what else to say. This is theology which sparkles."

Gypp and Johnny tinkered with the pianos at St. Nate's, Cassandra jotted down the best of it, and they mailed the score to Peterson with their blessings. A year later he had recorded it as *St. Nate's Cross*. Johnny played the track over and over again on Saturday afternoons at the O. Gypp would sit with his eyes squeezed shut and one hand moving as if his fingers were running across the keys. The sound poured over them. It was, Johnny said, another baptism, and Gypp nodded. The song lasted thirty-three minutes.

Johnny O's continued to bring in the best bands, Cassandra taught Slip to make cappuccino, Gypp sat in his corner, behind his screen, and wrote, if never again with the same intensity, yet with a flash and a verve and a temerity his sturdy and steady demeanour had scarcely shown before. Dusky Shrove and Sassy Usher brassed out the blues and smooned the smooths, the saxes and the noes wound up and around, and the bones and horns cleared the air while the drums drummed the earth.

Up at St. Nate's, Gypp and Johnny encouraged guitarists and bassists and flautists to join the saxophones and trombones and trumpets and the two pianos and the organ, and the church, the whole neighbourhood, began to rattle and nip and rip and roll. Hymns, psalms, and spiritual songs Gypp called them, Johnny called it St. Nate's Crossover, and if the ladies sang Amazing Grace or Sweet Chariot or Holy, Holy, Holy after Eucharist, this was holy ground, and the stone walls swelled with bodies and souls precisely where none of them had ever expected to be, surprised to stand among the angels and the sinuous sax players and a God with heart and soul and ten toes, surprised but counting themselves lucky to be fools, fools among the fools of greatest folly and greatest perception, the patron saints of jazz at St. Nate's, St. Nate's-among-the-fools.

CHAPTER

7

PANGUR BAN

"I will tell you exactly what it is. Christians prefer illusion to reality. So they do not want art and they certainly do not want fiction."

"But they will say fiction is the illusion, that it is lies."

"That's the great joke, isn't it? They fill their heads with silly stories, formula fiction that writers churn out like popcorn from a hot air popper. Then when a true piece of art comes along, a realistic bit of fiction, a story they can feel right down into their bones, they're afraid, and to ward that kind of story off, they start to argue that fiction is lies and not fit for a Christian mind."

"So they feel justified in ignoring it."

"They even feel righteous about it. That's why the most superficial nonsense is sold in bookstores. Reality is something Christians can't handle. A sugar-dusted spiritual romance they will buy and gobble up like candy. The Christian publishing houses oblige them. We wind up with a disembodied faith. No real touch, no real heart, no skin, no bone. They pop the romances and thrillers like narcotics and they get a buzz—they feel nothing real, see nothing real. It's their high. Honest-to-God fiction wouldn't do that. It keeps them on earth. It challenges them to face their own reality. No Christian wants to do that. So the romance is propped up by the Bible and fiction that talks about the real world is attacked or ignored."

"Well. The other arts hardly fare any better."

"No."

"The issue is honesty, isn't it, authenticity?"

"I think so. The paintings that are sold in the stores are nothing but placebos for Christians who can't cope with reality. Our stores and books and paintings and music, our churches, are hiding places. Not like hiding in God, mind you. There you are alert and aware of everything. Christianity's hiding places are like the old opium dens. You go there not only to get away from it all but to get drugged by it all and dwell, for as long as possible, in a pleasant artificial reality. But you become addicted. It kills you. It kills your soul. True Christianity ceases to exist in you. So the Christian faith has become a faith of addicts. And the faith itself is dead."

"It's almost midnight."

The talk ceased. Three women and four men sat in a circle before a red glimmering fire, the woodstove door open, the bricked room dark. They stared at a minute hand about to become one with the hour hand that was positioned at 12. The moment came. Outside the house they could hear people cheering and blowing horns and ringing bells. The seven of them knelt in prayer. A large man, his hair shaved off and a gold earring of a pen and a cross twinkling in the firelight, the one who had been doing most of the speaking, mumbled something in Latin and then began to pray in English.

"The problem is honesty, my Lord. Your people don't want it. They want smoke and mirrors. But you want spirit and truth. My God, look at the Book you gave us. Look at the music and the paintings and the poetry you have inspired in us in the past. Look how you shook the earth to the core with it. Look at how it remains with us, like running water cutting through the soil and brimming with the moon. How can your people continue to live in lies, my Lord? How can you carry mercy to the damned with a lie? How can you replenish the souls of your people? How can anything real be done when your people cringe from the real and welcome the hallucinogenic like a Saviour?"

He stuttered for words and fell silent. A woman at his elbow, as tall as he, big-boned and beautiful even in the dimness, her black hair pouring off her head and into her lap as she bent over, opened her mouth and prayed one sentence, "When, oh Lord, are you going to restore the kingdom?"

Another woman, her red hair in a buzz cut, lifted her lean face to the ceiling: "Give us plays of real power, Lord. Paintings that storm the imagination. Novels that bristle with light. Give us greys and primary colours. Give us raw images and give us subtleties. Didn't you speak to Bach and Hadyn? Didn't you give Eliot and Sayers and Lewis ink? What about the oils on Rembrandt's palette? God, God, can't you do that with us again?"

One of the men prayed, almost up out of her words, "What about your Bible? If you don't care about truth and art then why did you bother to write a masterpiece? If you don't care about beauty why did you fill Bezalel with the Holy Spirit to fashion the great patterns of your tabernacle? If you don't care, why give us Jubal and his flutes and his harps? Why give us the psalms? Why the splendour of the earth and why the elk and the butterflies and the panthers and the swans? Why the dragonfly? Why the prism and why the spectrum? Why the moon? Why Jupiter? Why the deepness? Why the fire?"

The third woman, as pale and faint as a night mist, whispered the final prayer, "We present our bodies and our souls to you as living sacrifices. Make us holy and make our art holy. Make it our worship. Alter us from the existing pattern, break our conformity to the bland and the commercial and the politically correct. Make us different. Make your people different. You wrote Job. You wrote the Song of Songs. You wrote John. Write us. Write this generation."

No more horns blared outside. They stood and embraced each other. "Happy New Thousand Years," smiled the man with the shaven head. "Bere'shith bara Elohim," said the tall black-haired woman. "Next Saturday evening then," reminded a man as thin and sharp as an ebony splinter. Outside the stars shimmered as if it were spring.

The church began in Peter and Linnea's house, the house they had prayed in, and Peter with his shaven head and earring and Linnea with her long black hair met their friends at the door. There was music with guitar and flute and congas. They read from the Bible in Hebrew and Greek and Latin and finally in King James English. They prayed. The woman of mist, Cara, did a slow dance as Linnea sang a song to Christ about his childhood in Egypt. The man of ebony, Simon, hung an oil of a beleaguered rainswept face entitled Noah. The woman with the short red hair, Marie, had woven a basket of willow laden with carved and painted wooden fruit that did not exist, blue pomegranates. She called the piece Aaron's Orchard. Her husband, Daniel, blonde hair to his shoulders, sipped ice water and red a poem he had written, Poppy. Peter sketched the woman at the well in stark charcoal on white paper while Eugene, small and round and unsmiling, read the story in Moffat's English translation.

For months this was a very satisfying arrangement. Poetry and sculpture and acrylics and every other form of art were brought in worship to

God and shared along with singing and prayer and the reading and relating of Scripture. But finally Eugene cleaned his glasses on his sweatshirt and expressed a deadness they were all feeling: "We are becoming elitist. God is for the world. So is his art. We have to go public."

So they found an old but spacious carpet showroom blessed with track and spot lighting and leased it. The street was busy and they were only a few blocks from the coffeehouses and galleries and dance studios. "I'm glad for the three blocks," said Peter. "It's everyone we want the art to touch. Not simply other artists or collectors." They called it The Studio Church or just The Studio, and it grew into a combination of many things, church, gallery, ballet class, writers' workshop, theatre. On Saturday nights it was ablaze and huge glass window after huge glass window allowed those walking by outside to see the singing and the dancing and the musical instruments gleaming, to see the dramas and mimes performed, to see fresh paintings being hung and displayed, to see a deeply burnished joy.

Others joined them, not just people from the artistic community or university students or professors, but truck drivers and cabbies and sales clerks and teenagers and mothers and fathers and families. All of them began to create, fine things that were placed on pedestals or sung in splendid tenors or danced between the rows of stacking chairs arranged neatly on lush blue carpet. People took turns opening The Studio to the public seven days a week. Some of the art was for sale—sketches, sculptures, engravings, there were racks of books the people themselves had written and which had been published locally, novels, short stories, fables. The first Christmas they acted out Menotti's Amahl and the Night Visitors, the second year they wrote and staged their own version of A Christmas Carol. Audiences sat on 150 chairs inside or stood out on the street, peering through the large show windows. There were summer nights for arias and duets, for baritones and tenors and sopranos, sidewalk cafes and street musicians and jugglers and actors, there was dancing at the park with the fountain just down the street, landscape and impressionist painting classes on the flat roof of The Studio. People learned how to see art and how to read literature and how to ride the swift currents of the spirit's depth, a ride and a depth which they grew to love after conquering their fear of what struck to the heart and made them alive to all that was.

Once The Studio became full on Saturday nights they went ahead and purchased an empty car showroom and stocked it with so much painting and sculpture they called it The Gallery Church. There were spin offs from both The Studio and The Gallery, all with their own names, all full of music and literature and everything else, all full of ordinary people who were starting to see extraordinary things and worship God who awed them with all the splendour of light breaking out of a prism. One new church in the downtown core was called The Gospel According to Jazz, another Go Down Moses, another The Church of Pangur Ban.

Simon, who revelled in all things Celtic, had taken the name Pangur Ban from a poem 1500 years old, written by an Irish monk who loved his God, his calling and his cat.

> I and Pangur Ban my cat
> 'Tis a like task we are at
> Hunting mice is his delight
> Hunting words I sit all night.
>
> Oftentimes a mouse will stray
> In the hero Pangur's way
> Oftentimes my keen thought set
> Takes a meaning in its net.
>
> When a mouse darts from its den
> O how glad is Pangur then
> O what gladness do I prove
> When I solve the doubts I love.
>
> So in peace our tasks we ply
> Pangur Ban, my cat, and I
> In our arts we find our bliss
> I have mine and he has his.
>
> Practice every day has made
> Pangur perfect in his trade
> I get wisdom day and night
> Turning darkness into light.

"Yes, I like the turning darkness into light bit," said Daniel. "But we need a crossover, you know."

"What do you mean?" asked Cara.

"The churches are wonderful. Bristling with honest life. But our paintings need to hang in other galleries. Our poetry needs to be sold in regular bookstores. We need to dance on other stages. Or we become a chain of glorified Christian supply stores frequented only by believers."

It became their mission. Not to the heart of Africa but to the heart of darkness of the postmodern world. Those that could were encouraged to find publishers that would take their books into all kinds of bookstores, or to hold shows in other galleries and pray that their works would be sold and hung not in museums of art but in banks and medical clinics and law firms. It began to happen, not overnight, but one woman published her novel with a publishing house that printed nice editions of Hemingway and Faulkner and Walker Percy. Another saw her impressionist painting of a woman's discovery of God and her rebirth hung at the international airport. Another danced two seasons with the city's ballet company. Another's sculpture of wolves and lambs and lions and calves and children playing together became the set piece for a new downtown park when a warehouse was demolished. Then artwork began to be sold in other cities and other countries. Some of the people received commissions to compose music and paint large canvases for large buildings and others were paid well to produce dramas for dinner theatre and the stage.

"The trick is to keep spirit and truth wedded," Linnea said to about one hundred of the leaders at The Studio. "Christ wedded to his art. No separation. Can we do that? If we can, then God blazes through the mind and imagination of our culture. If not, we are simply making Christianity a passing phase, another ghetto, sealed off in its own little world of delusion and make-believe."

"There must be much prayer," responded one man.

"Is there not enough?"

The man shrugged. "I know we meet. But does the mission become the god? Does the art become the Christ? Do we slap on the prayers for good luck? Or do we let them carry us? What forces wield the palette knife?"

Inevitably, the art outstripped the leaders' ability to keep up. It flew ahead in directions good and bad. Styles that had been original to The Studio or The Gallery or Pangur Ban were imitated by those who loved no Christ and worshipped no god but their own soul. The Christian bookstores The Studio had first turned its back on began to reproduce cheap copies in the style of the more successful paintings. These were accompanied by trite renderings of Scripture promises. Nevertheless, the surge that began at The Studio impacted and defied and wrestled postmodern art and created whole new ways of coming at truth and relativism and universals.

"The art of this movement, this rebellion," one critic suggested, "is laden with so many values, for the most part powerfully and disturbingly rendered, that what some are calling Post-Postmodernism might as well chase the monkey's tail back to the beginning and call this movement what it really is, which is Pre-Modern."

"You don't like it being called a movement, do you?" asked Simon, sipping a Pepsi and watching Peter slash at the monstrous canvas with a palette knife in a large white room at Pangur Ban.

"No."

"Some of it has even become trendy."

"That's happened before. It always happens. Can't be helped."

"It gets corrupted."

"We can't stop that, can we? There's enough of the real stuff going around."

"One critic called it the resurrection of the greatness of Western civilization."

"Why not call it what it is? The resurrection of Christ?"

"Some French magazine calls it "Le Nouveau Saint Esprit.""

"Why on earth does it need a French name?"

"To give it lustre."

"Eugene showed me a bunch of clippings from evangelical journals. They don't like much of our stuff, do they?"

"They like the happy art."

"Our lives are both. When are Christians going to come to grips with that and talk openly about it? The Bible is honest. We're supposed to be a people of the Book."

"They think the suffering and despair is too explicit. They say it's not good for people to dwell upon."

"Ah. So you skip Job. You skip Ecclesiastes. Lamentations. Half of Revelation. Half of the Psalms."

"Half of the Bible."

"So what don't they like besides Unanswered Prayer ?"

"Anything remotely like it."

In the black and white etching Unanswered Prayer a man in suit and tie, dishevelled, sat on the floor, slumped against his bed, half open venetian blinds striping a face bloated with misery. Far away on a wall was a crucifix.

"The evangelicals only want The Cross as a doctrine, Simon. Or a lucky charm."

"They never understood what Daniel was trying to do. Some Christians think he's saying prayer doesn't work."

"He's talking about a reality we've all experienced but no one wants to explore. The Cross was the result of an unanswered prayer, wasn't it?"

"They don't like my Job prints much."

"They're masterpieces. The best since Blake. Why did I gob that red there? Just remember what *Time* said about your prints."

"Some Christians think they're blasphemy."

"Some Christians don't think."

There were three prints, Job Chapter One, Job Chapter Two and Job Chapter Three. The first was a row of headstones and a man standing in his raincoat over them, his face bleak, his hand trailing a bouquet of flowers, the only objects of colour. The second was this same man crucified next to Christ in his tie and jacket while the person on the other side of Jesus howled with mirth and derision. The third print was Christ crucified alone. The print of his body was hung with actual trinkets and baubles the typical Christian bookstore sold and which Simon had purchased to festoon Christ with: Jesus action figures, good fortune angel pins, Jesus t-shirts, fridge magnets of the Cross, cheap imitations of Durer's praying hands.

"They like your series of paintings Sun on Houses, Simon."

"Yes. The one fellow said I made ordinary houses glow with the glory of the great cathedrals."

"There you are. Something is hitting home."

"But they hated Houses at Night. They said I'd been adversely influenced by Daniel's despair and my own mockery."

"People who exist solely within the realm of propaganda will always say that."

"They don't think we are modelling an attractive Christianity."

"And they are?"

"They love the stuff that's full of joy."

"They like bright colours. They'll love this piece. David's Dance. Not because they understand the God-depths of joy anymore than they understand the God-depths of suffering."

The canvas, twenty feet long by ten high, was a swirl and slap and spattering of hefty strokes of colour administered solely by Peter's palette knife. The painting seemed on the verge of jumping out of its borders and writhing on the floor.

"They want a world that is neat and tidy, Peter. One that makes sense."

"So let them read spreadsheets. Faith is a struggle. Faith is a drama. It's not a profession."

"What's that over against the far wall?"

"I'm putting another layer on later. That's Psalm 73."

"It looks like a concentration camp."

"I'm sure our evangelical friends will have a field day with it."

"And we're the evangelical fiends."

"Is that the new line now?"

"I just thought it up."

"Don't let them get ahold of it."

"I had a drama teacher once. Jewish. We were sitting around on the stage and he was giving us a pep talk. Art wasn't what you did after you did everything else that really mattered. Art was what really mattered. It wasn't the frosting on the cake. It was the very guts of human existence."

"You were blessed."

"I think so. We're so different from everyone else, Peter."

None of them had wanted the division that developed between those who "had art" and those who did not, but it happened just the same. Alternative Christian bookstores were opened. Some of the conventional ones withered but many had the supportive customers who loved the glitz and the gloss. Nevertheless, the conventional stores saw what was in the wind and had sections labelled ALTERNATIVE where they stocked the novels and the poetry and the music and some of the reproductions of the Noveau Spiritu Esprit.

Simon went over to take a closer look at the detail of Psalm 73.

"We'll die, Peter."

"I expect it."

"Who will paint the pictures and write the books? Aren't you afraid it will all revert to a plastic Jesus and a series of romantic novels five inches thick and skin deep?"

"We've caused enough of a furor. The torch is being passed. Look at Cybella Street and Newton Hart. They're running with it."

"A lot of bad artists are running with it. A lot of bad Christians are running with it."

"I told you. That always happens. Read the history of the great spiritual awakenings. Chaos and deception run right alongside and right through the best that God does. But there's a core of it that's always real. It re-emerges in surprising ways. We're not brand new, Simon. We started with Moses' tabernacle. No, we started with Creation. We're artists and God infused us with his power from the beginning of beginnings. No matter who tries to bury the real art, even if it's the churches, just like the understanding of God's grace and God's love that we keep losing, it'll keep popping up, generation after generation. The superficial and the mediocre won't disappear while we're on this earth. But neither will what is deep and profound."

"But this is an earthquake."

"Yes. I trust it's no mere crack in the pavement. I'm hoping this will move some mountains permanently."

"So we keep on engraving copper plates through the slings and arrows of outrageous fortune."

"And we try to turn darkness into light. What else is there?"

The paintings continued to go up on important walls, the novels continued to be written and sold alongside the other novels of the world. The dancers danced and the actors acted and the music found its way up crescendos and down descants. And photography also came in lines of silver and black and burstings of colour, and video and film came, not as teaching tools but as cinema that seized moviegoers by the heart and the soul and the mind. A million and another million who had never listened to a sermon, who had ripped up glossy tracts, who had shunned the bookstores and the concerts and churches of Christians, these—like Marie and Linnea and Cara's great bronze scultpture of a woman fighting a huge angel, the angel itself with a woman's face and limbs but with frightening, wondrous wings—these found themselves wrestling with God until a day broke in upon them and filled their windows and doorways with a towering cresset of light so that they finally lived and they finally walked, though with a mortal limp.

And they, the newborn of a hundred nations, crouched offstage, hearts hammering, before they stepped out under the burning lights and spoke their words, they stood before white canvases with their brushes and knives, intimidated and exhilarated, they sat at keyboards or scrawled lines on notepads in green forests and quiet city parks or forgotten corners of forgotten libraries. They wielded blowtorches like Eden's fire. Faces smudged with paint and grime, they prayed and fought through nights with stone and wood and iron. For the love of God, for the love of the creating, for the love of their freedom they painstakingly engraved plates, practiced a dance step over and over, filled their lungs and blew riffs with their horn night after night, chiselled marble, mixed rich oils that marked their skin and burned at the edges of their eyes, tossed and turned in sleep that would not come and finally offered their revelations to the turning earth.

CHAPTER

THE POETS OF
WINDHOVER MARSH

*with original poetry by Rod Peter, Linda & Murray
Pura, and Loren Wilkinson*

THEY GATHERED EVERY SUMMER at the cottage in the marsh because they knew the only hope for the Church and for the world was poetry and plenty of it. If God gave a resurgence of prayer, that was fine, as long as there was poetry in the prayers, however simple or stilted the words. If people felt they must repent, then they must do so, but let the repentance burn with sonnets and soliloquies, however halt, however lame. Let preaching be metaphor and simile and allegory and parable, let sermons rhyme and not rhyme, let there be sprung rhythm and running rhythm and inscape. Let Industrial Christianity come to an end. Rise, Blake! Let the Metaphysical Poets take the van! And you, Hopkins, remind us eloquently of the grandeur of God!

Too long has the Church groaned under the burden of men who spoke words that were blocks of wood. Were they true? In content, some, yes, but in spirit? Let us have women of substance now, whose words are winged, let us have the men, lit with flame, whose God is Truth, and whose sentences hurl sparks upon all the dead forests and brittle grasses of Christendom.

The Church speaks but there is no poetry, so her words fall lifeless and litter the earth. The Church cries in passion but there is no poetry, so no one knows of the heart on fire because no one can hear the voice. The Church argues and remonstrates against monstrosity and materialism but there is no poetry, so no one hears the archangel's shout above the roar of the satanic mills. The Church may formulate and articulate as precisely as she wishes. But without poetry, there are no words for what she believes, the vocabulary is impoverished and inadequate and obscene, the word of God is impossible. Without poetry, it is as if the Church never were.

So they believed. They gathered seven times a year at the marsh. But all of this actually began a long time before the 21st century. These poets were not the first. Squire Able Henry had purchased the marsh just before the civil war and Cromwell, who captured him, had let him keep it, even though the squire was a fervent royalist, because the property had no real value. It was north of the English border in the Scottish lowlands, there was no arable land unless you drained the marsh, and, well, it was just a swamp, wasn't it?

From the beginning it was called Galashiels Marsh, even though it was nowhere near Galashiels, then it was Moorfoot Marsh, which was a bit closer to home, then it was Pripkin's Marsh, Wynden Marsh, and finally Macleod's Marsh, the first time it bore a proper clan's name. A failed poet and successful naturalist by the name of Lovegrove bought it in the 1920's, because she loved marshes and she had a very great fear someone else would buy it, drain it, and plant brussel sprouts on it and a lot of other rubbish. There had always been a small stone cottage on the finger of land that poked into the marsh proper, a hunting cottage that went back to Culloden, at least, and she had a new slate roof put up, some sturdy black woodstoves moved into the two bedrooms, scoured boot sales in Edinburgh, Glasgow, and St. Andrews for furniture that could handle weight and substance (G.K. Chesterton was a close friend), and then she brought out naturalists to watch waterfowl in the marsh and talk about it, and she brought out poets to watch God in the marsh and write about it.

There was a legend that Hopkins had been there on a holiday from his teaching post at the Royal University in Dublin, the guest of a student named Macleod and his family, who at that time owned the marsh. This was never substantiated but Chesterton, who came there at Lovegrove's invitation six or seven times, was adamant about Lovegrove's sense of the thing and insisted the land must be held *in perpetua* as a poets' muse, and renamed in honour of the young Jesuit whose poems were just then becoming better known. He did not mean to offend the Scots by exchanging the Macleod title for another but it was holy ground. He recited many of his own poems at the cottage, seated in a great oak chair by the ancient hearth, a hearth a local man told them went back much farther than Culloden, took his meals at the massive table Lovegrove had wangled out of the owner of a down-at-the-mouth castle, and slept in a four poster bed (all the furniture held).

"Fools!" he thundered once on the grassy sward between cottage and marsh, so that a flock of mallards rose in alarm, squawking, to circle the forest and return. "I also had my hour, one far fierce hour and sweet, there was a shout about my ears, and palms before my feet." He penned a copy of the poem and began the tradition of poets leaving handwritten copies of their own poetry folded and stuffed into little niches between the stones inside the cottage walls. As this habit took hold among her guests, Lovegrove would let the poems be for a year and then unwad the papers and add them to her collection in a black book as large as a family Bible.

On Chesterton's last visit, he scrawled his favourite Hopkins poem on a sheet of parchment and Lovegrove framed that and placed it over the hearth. So the marsh was renamed Windhover Marsh, but following Chesterton's death in 1936 the cottage itself was forever after referred to as The Donkey. T.S. Eliot was fond of saying to friends in London, whenever he felt devoid of inspiration, "I need to journey north to visit the donkey," or, "Let us go up and ride the donkey." He travelled to Windhover Marsh often. A friend might join him at Lovegrove's insistence and Eliot would sit in one of the punts and let the friend ply the quant (you had to be good, the mud was like grasping hands). He wrote the better part of *The Four Quartets* there and all of *Burnt Norton*. Chesterton and Eliot spent a night in the cottage together in the early 30's, a time of candles and rich talk, that only ended with the dawn when both took paper and sat at the kitchen table and scribbled furiously in the white of the early light.

Many paths crossed at the marsh. Geese came and went, and grey blurred to green, while the poets made their journeys and listened to one another, and to the crickets, and ate the simple fare Lovegrove provided from the icebox and the stewing pot. Belloc finally came after Chesterton's death and met C.S. Lewis there, and John Masefield, and wrote *Courtesy,* which he read aloud at a fire where sparks flew to stars, "Our Lady out of Nazareth rode, it was her month of heavy load, yet was her face both great and kind, for Courtesy was in her mind."

Everyone loved Masefield's sea poems. Lewis was particularly fond of *Sea Fever,* but Masefield preferred to recite from *The Everlasting Mercy* and another longer poem he set down at the marsh's edge, "The wild duck, stringing through the sky, are south away. Their green necks glitter as they fly, the lake is grey. So still, so lone, the fowler never heeds. The wind goes rustle, rustle, through the reeds." He often ended the poem before its proper conclusion, staring at the fire or out the window as he spoke about Christ's crucifixion, "Darkness come down, cover a brave man's pain."

Charles Williams understood that sort of line. He came twice with Lewis, and once on his own for a month when he worked intensely on *The Region of the Summer Stars,* completing it shortly before his untimely death in 1945. He loved it when the marsh misted and he watched one long summer evening as the stars burnt white-hot holes through it. J.R.R. Tolkien didn't care to come when Williams was there. He showed up once in Lewis' company before their falling out and another time with his son Christopher at the height of a storm. Gollum was created there, so he confided to Lovegrove, and he confessed that a good deal of *The Ring* had taken shape and substance where reeds and murk met. "The bog," he called it cheerfully, and Masefield never forgot working on *Good Friday* at a card table set up outside the cottage door, and glancing up to see Tolkien, pipe billowing, hunched over in a punt with a pad of paper, pounding a rhythm with one gnarled fist and jotting down one of the hobbit songs with the other, all the time the punt spinning and drifting over the entire marsh.

Dorothy came up three or four times too, on her own or with a lady friend. She stayed in her bedroom one whole day to get a good start on *The Zeal of Thy House,* but most remember her huddling by the hearth in a great shawl when she was being bitterly attacked for writing up a Jesus who spoke modern English in her radio play. The last broadcast was during the height of the Stalingrad battle, October 18th, 1942, and people were in a dark mood anyway, but she took some fearful stones. Lovegrove fed her copious amounts of tea and thick slices of fresh bread she had baked in a special pot, a sort of Dutch Oven, right in the fire. Dorothy would mutter something about this when she was down south and rattling through a tough go with Lord Peter Wimsey: "Bread, Lovegrove, bread, something God-wrought to sustain me."

It was an incredible century at The Donkey, poet laureates like Masefield knotted in thought, and Robert Bridges too, clutching hardboiled eggs and a shaker of salt, with his "Whither away, fair rover, and what thy quest?", trading sea stories and sea shanties with John, refusing to confirm or deny the legend about his friend Hopkins and the marsh, but leaving with Lovegrove as a special gift a 1918 first edition of the Hopkins poems that he had collected. There was Lewis with his ale, wading into the marsh up to his knees, pipe clenched between his teeth and reciting *No Beauty We Could Desire,* as if he was attempting to be heard over a street brawl in Belfast. There was even Robert Graves, cloistering himself for a week and dashing off *In The Wilderness,* a poem about Jesus' forty days of temptation—"He held communion with the she-pelican"—but refusing to explain which way his spirit was leaning when he left. It all ended too soon. Belloc dead in '53—"My Rhyme is written, my work is done"—Lewis in '63, Tolkien in '73, Dorothy in '57, Masefield in '67. They weren't the only ones of course, just some of the principal players.

A chap at Peebles finally told Lovegrove on her own deathbed that his grandad had seen Robert and Elizabeth Browning at the marsh in the 1850's, when the old man had been hunched over in a blind waiting for a shot at some ducks. The Brownings had never seen him, but they stayed at the cottage the entire morning and not a mallard landed for grandad, even with the fine decoys he'd carved and painted the winter before. Elizabeth fished one out of the water and walked away with it, and the old chap didn't have the nerve to step out of his camouflage and ask for it back. He met them in a tavern a week later and that's how he found out who they were.

It was as splendid as a deathbed can be for Lovegrove. A white-haired gentleman dropped by and related how, as a young boy catching tadpoles and frogs at the marsh, he'd met George MacDonald on a sunny afternoon in 1902. MacDonald sat down with him and told him a bit of whimsey, a story of a princess and a grand dragonfly, which no one has ever seen in print, and explained that he came down to the cottage to rewrite his poems and fantasies, since they always turned out better the second time if he took a stab at them by Macleod's Marsh. Lovegroved died contented. She was buried in what she called holy ground, just off from The Donkey in a grove of willows, flashing a sun's bright gold when they put up her stone: *LOVEGROVE. Give me but these, and though the darkness close even the night will blossom as the rose.* A line from Masefield, already gone.

After her came the quiet years, though there's no denying poets made their way to the cottage. The locals knew. They clipped the grass and put a block of ice in the icebox along with some victuals once a week, and they left cookies and pies they'd baked, and fresh cream. A poet might starve for words but not for shortbread and biscuits at Windhover Marsh. Still and all, the years were lean compared with the holy foam and ferment of the decades before.

It wasn't until early in the next century that a crowd began to gather again, in God's time, they said, and these explained some thirty years dearth on a world smothering God and God's poetry, and a Church that went along with it, preferring the God of the limited vocabulary and the trite slogan, rather than the great God of smoke and blood, the fine shining God of the singing liturgies and the deep-running creeds. Though the whole lot of them disliked agendas, they had one just the same. "God created the world by imagination!" they cried, echoing Nicholas Berdyaev, the Russian religious philosopher and emigre, whom many swore had made the trek from Paris to Windhover Marsh sometime in the 1930s.

They felt the earth would never turn on conventional apologetic, not in two-double oh-two, and they shared a heartsfire to infuse the Church and her spirituality and her theology with the earth, wind, and fire of a poet laureate. They were much more of an association than the poets had been in the twentieth century, calling upon everyone to meet at The Donkey seven times a year, and they even had a motto, *non verba sed tonitrua, not words but thunderclaps.* Women and men came in from all over the world for The Seven, not hundreds, but no gathering lacked a quorum of twelve. Poets came at other times, of course, back and forth every season of the year, but no one wanted to miss The Seven, it did your soul such good and crammed your notebooks with shooting stars.

Who replaced Lovegrove? Partridge did. God knows where he came from (none of the poets did), but he was splendid at chopping wood, repairing punts, brewing tea and baking scones, and he delighted in proffering mince pies on any Sunday between All Saints Day and Lent. He knew Lovegrove's traditions and the folded poetry in the cracks whitened the interior walls. If a poet was discouraged, Partridge was there with tea and good cheer. If a poet needed words, Partridge offered to ply the quant and slip them between the lilypads and the blackbirds. Did they lack faith? Partridge opened the Family Bible, as the ancient collection of poems was called. Did they need prayer, Partridge knelt. Did one desire a homily from the Good Book, Partridge did that, quietly but with a tethered fire. If there was hunger, how did he do it, Partridge carved roast fowl and rotisseried duck, but he never harmed the feather of any bird that called the marsh home for a night or for a lifetime.

There were five poets that were particularly important at Windhover Marsh in the first half of the 21st century, Malcolm St. Michaels, Roman

Greene, Andrew Becket-Burns, Rowena Cove, and Heather Mary Cameron. Becket-Burns and Cameron were the most intense of them all when it came to expostulation—"We must have a rolling ripe theology!"—but all five could gutter a candle when it came to night writing or what Greene called "star scribble". In other generations the poets had merely plied their trade to the glory of God and had no plans to inundate the earth. But the new breed wanted theologians to write like MacDonald or Lewis and preachers to preach like John Donne or Lancelot Andrewes, or at least exhibit the eloquent pithiness of Bunyan. Their own poems hung like ruby pendants with God's weight or darted like starlings with his spirit, so that there rose the expression in Christendom of *Roman, Rowena, and Heather contra mundi.*

They swayed some, they could not sway all, yet there is no question that as Athanasius preserved the Trinity, the poets preserved linguistic beauty and reinstated theology as the Queen of the Sciences. They dusted her off and burnished her and made her shine like Victoria of old. She was quicksilver through the West again, a queen of all the peoples of the earth, no more an academic's plaything. For many years, certainly until 2060 or later, it was impossible to stand up at Oxford or Cambridge or St. Andrews or King's and speak like a block of wood. If you wished to be obfuscatory, you had better be a jolly Shakespeare at it, for truth became so wrapped up in the precise and crystalline language of the poet, it was impossible to get a posting at any school that made a fig of a difference on earth without a laureate's panache and a filigree turn of phrase.

It was not simply about eloquence alone, about stringing pretty words together. Truth and significance had to entwine your prose and your passion. Nor was complexity an honour. If it all went somewhere and did so splendidly, well and good. But labyrinthine casuistry that lit lanterns to nowhere made no lasting impression. A man might write with the simplicity of Aesop, but if he had Aesop's wisdom and Aesop's spare eloquence, why then, he stood alongside not only Christ's plain parables but Augustine's *City of God.*

One journal called it the resurrection and revolt of the Metaphysical Poets and perhaps it was that. At the height of the furor, from 2013 to 2027, when all the marsh poets, not just The Five, needed to hear from an angel of God to sustain them, Partridge was planting a border of rosebushes and flowering herbs right around the cottage. At the front and back door he wished to place fresh flagstones, since the old ones had cracked so often they were like chunks of gravel. As his spade pried the pieces out and he dug past them to loosen the soil at the front door, there was a ringing as iron struck iron. Partridge bent over, saw it was a strongbox, and swiftly unearthed it. St. Michaels and Greene came from around the back where they had been setting up hoops for croquet when they heard Partridge shout.

"It's locked," noted Greene.

"I've got a hacksaw," panted Partridge, and he went to the small stone toolshed Lovegrove and Belloc had mortared in 1948.

"Perhaps we don't want to open it," cautioned Greene.

"Whyever not?" Partridge was incredulous.

"You know. Pandora's box."

St. Michaels snorted and gripped the bowl of his pipe, a bowl as big as a small ham. "For heaven's sake, Roman, what do you think, the curse of the mummy will come against us? This is Scotland, man."

Roman crossed his arms. "Scotland is a queer bird."

St. Michaels waved his pipe. "Welcome to your gory bed or to victory, Roman. Open it, Partridge."

Partridge had paid their quibbling no mind. He was groundskeeper and tender of the hearth. They just wrote things. The thick padlock came away in a few minutes, sweat popping on Partridge's arms and face.

"Right then." He opened the black iron lid.

"No monkey's paw, Roman," grunted St. Michaels as he bent to look. Partridge had pulled back a frayed and yellowed cotton cloth. "Just paper."

Roman remained aloof. "Whose?"

Partridge was reluctant to touch the stack of papers with his dirty hands so St. Michaels lifted a sheaf of them and studied them for a few moments.

"Well, Malcolm?" demanded Partridge.

"Impossible," St. Michaels muttered, looking at page after page. He gave six or seven of them to Greene. "What do you make of this, Roman?"

Roman took them with no desire to appear interested or impressed. But after glancing at three of the pages his blue eyes opened from indifferent slits to great orbs of astoundment.

"I don't believe this!" he snapped. "Partridge, did you put this here? Is this some sort of prank?"

Partridge daggered his eyebrows. "I am not a trickster, sir."

"But this is impossible."

"What are they?" Partridge finally got to his feet. He tried to take one of the papers but Greene jerked it away.

"Wash your hands!"

Partridge had no running water to work with at the cottage but there was a freshwater stream, resplendent with mixed salmon trout, which flowed into the marsh and from which he fetched water for tea or cooking or cleaning. He rinsed his hands there now and dried them thoroughly on the long green grass at the stream bank, then hurried back. St. Michaels was kneeling and riffling through the rest of the box, his pipe jammed into a shirt pocket still smoking, while Greene stood where he was, scanning whatever St. Michaels passed up to him.

"Extraordinary," Greene murmured.

"Give me one!" Partridge snatched a paper from Greene. It was stiff paper and heavy, and it had a bit of yellowing. There was writing and it was dark but faded in a few places, like old fountain pen ink. He attempted to decipher the scrawl.

"Therefore that he may raise the Lord throws down," he read out loud. Greene looked at him.

"It can't be!" protested Partridge.

"Well, then," responded Greene, "what do you make of this one?"

More of the same scrawl. Partridge squinted. "Batter my heart, three personed God. For you as yet but knock, breathe, shine, and seek to mend. No!"

"Or this?" St. Michaels handed up several pages of the same sort of paper but the writing was completely different.

"Reversed thunder," read Partridge, struggling, "Christ-side-piercing spear . . . church-bells beyond the stars heard, the soul's blood, the land of spices, something understood. God in heaven!" This last was Partridge's shriek.

"What do you think?" asked Greene.

"But these are originals!"

"Malcolm and I think so."

"God in heaven! Who else is there besides Donne and Herbert?"

"Malcolm has pulled up Marvell, you'd expect that. But there's Blake too. Spenser. And look at this."

Greene held out a thick sheaf of papers that had been bound by a ribbon which disintegrated as soon as St. Michaels had attempted to loosen it. Yet another hand had penned this. Partridge held the first sheet up to the sunlight.

"I can't make it out. Ah! Till one greater Man restore us, and regain the blissful seat. Do you mean to say?" He quickly brought up the last sheet and scowled at the final lines: "They, hand in hand, with wandering steps and slow through Eden took their solitary way. The whole poem? All of it in Milton's hand?"

"Or someone's. I don't know Milton's hand myself," said St. Michaels getting to his feet. "Do either of you know Spanish? Or Latin?"

"Cove knows the Spaniards," answered Partridge. "She winters near Madrid when she can. What is it?"

"Something about death, isn't it?" suggested Greene, peering over St. Michaels' shoulder. "Que muero porque no muero?"

"Becket-Burns knows Italian. Did a thesis on Italian poets at St. Andrews."

"Where is he?" asked St. Michaels.

"Iona. On retreat. He'll be up for next week's Seven."

"Then we will have to wait until he and Cove show up." St. Michaels put his papers back in the iron box. "A touch from God, I think, gentlemen. Croquet, Roman?"

"It's hardly appropriate."

"What? God becomes man and you can't play croquet after a visitation?"

"Did Mary?"

A week later fifteen of them sat with kerosene lamps distributed among them burning hotly. Cove had just finished speaking when Partridge bustled through the door with some sticks for kindling.

"Put it down, P!" Cameron shot. "Did you hear what Cove said?"

"Of course not."

"We don't need a fire. Your lamps are roasting us. Que meuro porque no meuro. En mi yo no uiuo ya y sin Dios biuir no puedo."

Partridge was peevish, he'd wasted time getting wood for a fire no one wanted. "So?"

"Dying for my dying day," recited Cove. "Life within me? Not a spark. Without God's a deadly dark! It's San Juan de' la Cruz."

"It is not!"

"It is P!" This from Cameron.

"And what about that other? That great thick bit that was wrapped in leather?"

"We're just getting to it. BB has been looking at the whole thing."

Becket-Burns got to his feet, still staring down at the manuscript he held in both hands. He didn't look up. "I've been going over it since St. Michaels gave it to me last night. Listen to this: La gloria di colui che tutto move per l'universo penetra e risplende in una parte piu e meno altrove. Nel ciel che piu della sua luce prende fu'io, e vidi cose che ridire—The glory of Him who moves all things penetrates the universe and shines in one part more and in another less. I was in the heaven that most receives his light and I saw things . . . It's the opening cento of *Paradiso.*"

"Surely it's not an original?" asked one of the poets.

"I've studied Dante. I can't say I know his hand. But this is the original Italian text. The whole *Comedy* is here."

The night had been overwhelming for everyone but Partridge, Greene, and St. Michaels who had already been overwhelmed and had had several days to try to get used to it.

"You mean to say you think Dante came up here and just left the *Comedy* in a stone hut in Scotland?" asked another poet.

"Or someone brought the manuscript up here from Italy with Dante's blessing." Becket-Burns shrugged.

"Or stole it?"

"No!" barked Partridge. "This is holy ground. The poets and their own words come here. No one knows about this place except an angel tells them."

"Well, BB told me."

They laughed but another poet broke through the merriment.

"It looks like a hoax."

Roman Greene stood up. "Yes, Malcolm and I thought about that. But who would have perpetrated such a hoax? Would Chesterton have done this? Or Eliot? Or Masefield? Could you accuse any of them of such chicanery?"

The poet's face soured. "Well, a local then."

"What? A farming lad from Moffat or Tinto Hill? Using different handwriting? Using Spanish and Italian? Writing out hundreds of pages of Milton and Dante and St. John of the Cross? To what purpose? To trick us into inspiration? What is the effect of having these old poets among us? Does it enervate us? No, there is a flash flood in your blood to go further and to strike deeper with all your words."

St. Michaels was cramming his pipe bowl with tobacco from a leather pouch. "At any rate, we were up to Edinburgh to have an expert look at the paper. All of it's hundreds of years old. No one makes paper like that anymore. All the writing's in old mixes of ink and done with quill. The fellow was astounded. Wanted to know how we came to have the poetry. I think he thought we'd pinched it from a museum. He said he was going in the back room to ring up a colleague but Roman and I were sure he was calling the police. So we left in a hurry." St. Michaels snorted as the pipe gushed a pillar of fire. "Different quills too. Different birds. Different parts of Europe."

Rowena Cove smiled. "It's a miracle then."

"What shall we do with them?"

"We ought to give them to Oxford or Cambridge or to the British Museum."

"No poetry leaves the marsh," declared Partridge.

"But they'll deteriorate here."

"They've done pretty well for a few hundred years," St. Michaels growled around his pipe stem. "The box was pretty much airtight. I'm sure Partridge can preserve them adequately."

"But they're relics."

"All the more reason they should be here."

"Are we sure?"

Partridge began to remonstrate in the chiaroscuro of the ancient stone cottage, the sheaves of the old poetry scattered about the room in people's laps. "This is not our decision. Its been made for us. Do you imagine I or any of us have the rights over Chesterton's poems that he left here, or Belloc's, or Tolkien's? They meant for them to be here. We didn't know about the strongbox. But hundreds of years ago those poets found this place because God intended for them to find this place, and they left their poems here because God intended for them to leave their poems here. I've told you, this is a holy place. This is a great cathedral, one of the wonders of the world, it took a thousand generations to build it. After we've gone God will continue to bring poets here so that he can inspire them, and replenish the Church with their words, and revitalize the earth. Isn't that what we're doing now? Isn't that what others will be doing in a hundred years? Is there anyone here who doesn't want to get off on their own right now and write a poem, perhaps one of the best they've ever written? Why? Because you know the good Lord Christ is in this, don't you? You can read his lines, you know his hand, we all do. This is no serendipity. You were meant to find these poems and draw fresh fire from them to ignite your own verse. All of the poetry must remain at the cottage, every page of it, old and new. A woman will be drawn here at the turn of this century, a woman from Brazil who will scarcely know what she's about, but she'll find your poem, Heather, or one of yours Rowena, or even one of yours, BB, and she'll take heart and clutch a pen and write with pinions and theophanies and all the scalding cascades of light. This is God's doing and we dare not seek to undo it."

No one stirred. Until St. Michaels stretched and climbed out of his chair. "I don't know about anyone else, but I have work to do before the night is spent. It's time for some star scribble. Roman?"

Greene, with his black turtleneck and tightly curling black hair and pierce-the-dark blue eyes, was staring directly into a lamp. "It's true," he said.

So they broke up and found their niches and began to write. Partridge scurried about brewing coffee and tea and baking fresh scones. It was summer but he fashioned some mince pies anyway. Once dawn pelted them with bright stones and the writers grew weary and sore, Partridge had everything ready for bed.

To begin with, he had altered both the bedrooms months before. Now one was for men, the other for women, and each had bunk beds and linen for four. Then he had eight cots. If he had a mix of men and women, as he did for that Seven, he put up a line between the walls of the cottage and strung blankets. It didn't take long for everyone to settle in. Heather Mary Cameron snored with ferocity.

"Heaven help us," sniffed Partridge, moving his bed linen to the tool-shed. "The pipes."

Partridge had closed up the privy he had dug ten years before and reopened the one Lovegrove and Lewis and Tolkien had built up with field stone and mortared together in 1954. Lovegrove had penned a note about it in the Family Bible: "A very hot day. The loo almost done. Jack and Ronny mucking about, quaffing ale and guffawing, did me good to see it. They got into a mock sword fight with their trowels, both of them shouting out rubbish in Latin, dotty old men, spotted their faces and clothing with mortar, then sat and had a pipe and went on about King Arthur till sunset, when they asked me to spear portions of fresh Angus on green sticks so they could cook them over a fire. A lad from Motherwell had brought the beef by that morning. Ronny quite proud of them building the fire up from scratch. They were on about the Old Norse language and archangels and what sort of steel was in the swords the apostles wore at the crucifixion. Went to bed and they were singing lustily in West Saxon, beating the rhythm on the ground with great sticks that showered the sward with orange sparks. Woke at dawn and they were still up. They had caught some fish in the stream, which they named Oxblood, and were at grilling them over their precious fire. Wondered how our Lord had cooked his fish on the beach at the resurrection. Swore to me in Latin that they would finish up the loo after breakfast and then fell asleep under the willow. Used the old plaid blankets with the MacDonald tartan. Expect they'll rise from the dead with the moon. Midsummer's Day."

The privy was in the round and you could see CSL stroked in the mortar between two stones and the trace of a lion's head, while nearby a finger had poked JRR with a lot of runic characters. There were two separate compartments. It had been used through the last half of the 20th century, the pits were deep, much had decomposed, and once Partridge had cleared off twenty-five years of blackberry thorn the poets used it gladly. By common consent they nicknamed the two compartments Gollum and Marsh-wiggle.

No one who was there for that Seven ever forgot it. They wrote some of their finest poems and returned to their churches and academies to inspire others, so that a kind of divine prose flared over Christendom that scorched the heart of the earth. It became a season of Eucharist and Redemption. It exhilarated. Of a certainty, there were stepping stones between earth and heaven, between wind and fire, between Christ and marsh.

Each of the Five wrote a poem and folded it away into the venerable grey walls that week. In time, of course, Partridge plucked them free and smoothed them down into the Family Bible. He placed them one after the other, beginning with Becket-Burns. BB had called his *The Eucharist of the Fall.*

a season now
frescoed
a thousand pietas
losing all and lost
and ageing, greying
and barren, bereft
losing all and lost
but the losing in the losing
twice gold, thrice gold
sun, tree, and spotted grass

all diving, rising
a ripe orchard
a ripe orchard's harvest
bright apple round peach
lights and lights and lights
flying
whether owl or kingfisher or wren
or leaf or branch or root
upon the green water lying
till all dying
is light, is flight
till knowing this brightwork
is right, is God's right

Rowena Cove wrote *Twelfthtide*.

harvest moon	honey moon
hunter's moon	devil moon
blue moon	december moon
christ's moon	

the sands	the wood
the two walk	etched in chalk

each ocean drop	beneath the fire
holds high its	singing candle
the processional	to the shore

Heather Mary Cameron made noise when she wrote, as if each syllable was wrested or pried violently out of her soul, and she wrote with both
fists clenched, for the whole process of putting her poetry on paper was a
battle and a hammering, and her eyes glinted and her cheeks filled with
blood, and she crumpled paper and she stabbed with her pen, and sometimes roared. The poem she left behind she sealed with tape, a seal that
only Partridge broke. She called it *Lament*. Only two stanzas of it were
legible.

Your children
play with stones
stained with ancestral blood
they dance in streets
paved with judgement.

O Israel, child of holy promise
your destitute ways
your tattered soul
tears painfully
at the heart of a grieving God.

Roman Greene gave no title to his. He put it down in fountain pen ink, folded the ivory paper neatly, slipped it into a hole by the front door, and quietly went on his way.

I would to speak a thousand times
the words I hold so dear,
but thousands times a thousands times
their message seems unclear.
Tis not the words themselves be rough
though kinder could they be,
it be the form that seeks their depth
that hides their sympathy.
A man like any man is he
who bends those pretty words,
to straggled heaps of shapeless dreams
and deeds of lesser worth.
But yet to speak those dear dear words
is what my being cries,
to live their fate and breath their flame
tis here my heart's hope flies.
So thus to say I love you dear
does set this heart at ease,
and should I live till earth dies old
these words I'll try to please.

Malcolm St. Michaels found a stump in the woods over beyond the marsh and wrote there, wreathed in Scotch mist, cinders from his ubiquitous pipe burning fine black holes through his verse.

February, and time to burn the Christmas tree
(Dropping needles in its desolate corner).
In December, already dying, it hinted still
Of green wilderness, and we hung our family's past
On its resinous bounty.
(Noriko's origami stars; Judy's sheep;
From Whidbey Island, Andy's painted pins;
Crocheted snowflakes from Lola on the Greensprings,
And Bruce and Robin's lion and lamb,
Still peaceful in their play-dough wreath.)
But now not even the coloured lights
Can hide the spiderwebs, the brown.
So put the relics all back in their boxes
And with a hatchet lop the limbs
Till the trunk stands naked in its bucket.
Burn them all night long in the orange roar, The flaming sword, of
long-gone Eden:
Burn them like straw in the flame that burns
At the heart of things with the unsung names
Of the one who is,
Burn the pine like frankincense:
That baby too grew up to be consumed.
You and I will sleep
On this warm hearth's holy ground
And in the morning mark our heads with ash.

He called it *Burning the Christmas Tree.* In due time, Partridge laid it in the great book with the others, with Lewis and Bridges and Williams and Greene, neat and white and dark-spotted.

So they changed the world. Or rather, God shaped a new world out of the words, out of their words and his words, out of the poetry of cross and resurrection and epiphany, out of blood and clay and light, and they all died except St. Michaels, who buried Partridge by Lovegrove and took his place, brewing tea and stirring soup and pruning rosebushes for another generation who made their way in fits and starts to Windhover Marsh. St. Michaels puttered about the cottage and grounds, showed the new poets the Family Bible and the Strongbox, and blew storms of spark and thunder from his pipe as they wept and slept and rose and wrote and fashioned streams of streaming sunlight and told of a dying and rising God who was beyond all words, beyond creation, beyond fashioning, and beyond them. And sometimes St. Michaels would open an old and dark Bible, Blake's it had been, and read out loud, usually by the hearth, whether lit or cold, and St. Michaels dearly loved St. John and the Christ in reeds and rushes there. And post sometimes came to Windhover Marsh from Peebles and if poets asked how to find the cottage, St. Michaels would write, *Come down by way of Holy Island, by way of the Lammermuir Hills and the Moorfoot Hills and the Tweedsmuir Hills, come down by way of County Lothian and County Borders, by way of Peebles and Galashiels, come down by way of Lough St. Mary's and you will make out all right.*

St. Michaels was at home at the marsh. It is true that there were days and even weeks when it was just he and the waterfowl and butterflies fuller than your spread hand and the cooling Scotch mist and bright heaven's sun. These were fine times to pray and to worship and to wander. His mind would tumble and turn with the words of all the poets who had ever come to Windhover Marsh and he jotted down a bit of doggerel about it.

a thousand poems he had read
a hundred of the thousand stormed daily through his head
Blake and Donne and Thomas Stearns
Masefield and Dante and Becket-Burns
up and up and over the ark
to hear the song of the Hopkins lark

in crisps of curl off wild winch whirl
look at the stars! look, look up at the skies!
o look at all the fire-folk sitting in the air!
the bright boroughs, the circle-citadels there!
in what distant deeps or skies
burnt the fire of thine own eyes?
on what wings dare he aspire?
what the hand dare seize the fire?

for I, except you enthrall me
never shall be free
nor ever chaste
except you ravish me

what? is it all one?
is he, the three, truly one?
and his poets
whether Hopkins, Blake, or Donne
all one, truly one?
and we and all we write
the wit of his Son?

St. Michaels would take out a punt or tug on his wellies and circum-navigate Tolkien's "bog" and Spenser's "reeking swamp". There was much to see and the angle of light over the far hills was always not as it had been and he prised from the muck and rushes what he never knew. A shoe, whose? A pen that wrote, what? A cup and saucer, Royal Doulton, a pattern not known. One day, a long-necked brown bottle. Black letter-ing had been painted on it and was legible. *TO BYZANTIUM BY WAY OF SEA AND MARSH ON HIS MAJESTY'S SERVICE.* The bottle was stop-pered with a rubber cork and papers were rolled tightly within. St. Michaels had to lay aside his pipe and completely destroy the cork before he could get at them. They turned out to be poems. A bit of water had trickled in and smeared some ink but for the most part the poetry was sharp and readable.

Chesterton was writing: *So we commit these to the deep until the sea shall give up what needs be read.*

The first poem was Hopkins, but not in Chesterton's hand, *Inversnaid, This darksome burn, horseback brown, his rollock highroad roaring down, in coop and in comb the fleece of his foam flutes and low to the lake falls home, degged with dew, dappled with dew are the groins of the braes that the brook treads through, wiry heathpacks, flitches of fern, and the beadbonny ash that sits over the burn.*

The next was MacDonald, in MacDonald's own hand and signed, *Thy fishes breathe but where thy waters roll, thy birds fly but within thy airy sea, my soul breathes only in thy infinite soul, I breathe, I think, I live but*

*thee, oh, breathe, oh, sink—O Love, live into me, unworthy is my life till
all divine, till thou see in me only what is thine.*

The final sheet was more of Chesterton's scrawl, which he titled *A
Prayer in God's Good Light*, but which has come down to us under a different name. St. Michaels framed all three fragments, what had not been
obliterated or damaged by marsh water, and placed them on the walls of
The Donkey, The Windhover already hanging over the fire.

So it came to be that when a poet picked his way over briar and
unmortared wall, when she came down by way of Lothian and Borders
and Peebles and Galashiels, when he opened the stout door the Tinker
himself had nailed sturdy and true, betwixt and between the writing of a
pearl that "may in a toad's head dwell", when she ate and drank and slept,
and there was Hopkins on the two long walls, and when he went out to the
back door to write, all flicker and faint, there was MacDonald on his way
for courage, and then, in due time, the turning time, time to leave the valley and the stones and the marsh and the fire-folk sitting there, back out
the Tinker's door to heaven and hell and all angels, she would pause, and
see perhaps for the first time the small frame of willow branch and the bit
of Chesterton scribble there and she, in her pause, could read and not forget, and in this the poetry of her spirit should live and those that chose, on
the turning earth, live and live and live, even if upon a dark is layered a
dark and another dark. And they would turn when they read it, to look
back at St. Michaels, to look back at the open door, open on the marsh,
and then go on down the road in the gloaming to Peebles and Galashiels
and the Moorfoot Hills and the Holy Island and the great seas and somewhere, to a quiet garden by a humming water, to sit and write beautiful
truths beautifully, and give it back, oh give it back, *give beauty back,
beauty, beauty, beauty, back to God, beauty's self and beauty's giver,* and
think of Chesterton thumping along by the shore, swishing rushes with his
cane in the dark falling world, tempted perhaps to never write again, to
never try again, and then standing still in the evening damp of wonder, *for
men say the sun was darkened, yet I had thoughts it beat brightly, even on
Calvary, and he that hung upon the torturing Tree heard all the crickets
singing, and was glad.* Christ's last word to parting poets.

And so tired, I am tired, my God but I am tired, but I am glad, so very glad, I am glad I was here when and when and when. And then St. Michaels went through the reeds and the trees round by the marsh and up past the marsh to the sward of thick green grass and so to the cottage, old, old, to write a word and drink a cup of tea and to see God sitting at the hearth and the stones and their poems ringing and an earth coming free and a liberty steeped in burnished mists a-day-a-day's walk from Long Forties and the North Sea and Devil's Hole and Lindisfarne Mystery, a Farne Deep and a love to sing, and Lewis' words and their Eden ring, and closed round by these great grey stones, I see, I see, and from out of the earth and these Scottish mists the poets come to me.

All this, indeed, I do not remember.
I remember the remembering, when first walking
I heard the golden gates behind me
Fall to, shut fast. On the flinty road,
Black-frosty, blown on with an eastern wind,
I found my feet. Forth on journey,
Gathering this garment over aching bones,
I went. I wander still.
But the world is round.

CHAPTER

LAST NIGHT'S TRAIN
TO LUCKNOW

Dear Dad,

We got on last night's train to Lucknow, but not so easily. We were locked out of our sleeper car and I was afraid the train would pull out without Curtis or I. We had to yell a lot to get the tickets in the first place. Now we yelled some more. The car got unlocked, we got our gear stowed and climbed into our berths, just cots near the ceiling above the other seats. We were kicked out of there to two other berths. Stretched out. Lots of noise all night, yet I slept.

Lucknow at 7.30 AM. Out with our baggage, especially the reason for this whole trip, the big wooden box of Chinese Bibles for the missionaries in Kathmandu. We promised the mission we used as a hostel in New Delhi we'd take them over the border to Nepal. It's out of our way but we want to see the country. Riding the rails of India is supposed to be a treat.

So Curtis and I jammed ourselves into a bicycle rickshaw. Pedal. Getting tickets for the A.T. Mail. We lined up at one window, waiting for the ticket booth to open. We were first in line but all the people that came after us made their own line beside us that stretched for blocks. Finally a man approached us and told us we were in the wrong line and that we would have to go to the end of the other line. I told him we had been first and that ours was the correct line. Curtis and I remained in our two man line-up. When the iron shutters of the ticket window finally slid up we swooped and so did the rest of Lucknow. It was chaos. But we pressed our way to the window, ignoring attempts to elbow us away from the booth, trample us or by any means dislodge us. We purchased our tickets and considered ourselves the most fortunate of men. But then we had to try to find room on the train.

In India there is now only first or second class. We always take second—so does the rest of India. (Might as well say the rest of the world.) After much battling and pleading and jostling, we finally just sat down inside a doorway with some others. All the cars were packed, people even wedged in the windows. The train pulled out and I sat legs dangling in the open door. One of the best train trips I've ever had.

Lots of air, lots of green and yellow scenery, but the engine was a locomotive, as all of them tend to be, and by the time the trip to Gorkhapur was over, I looked like I'd just climbed out of a coal mine. As the wind created by the train's movement had flowed over me, rendering the Indian heat tolerable, so had the black smoke and fiery cinders, a spark dropping down the collar of my T-shirt once and causing me to jump. The soot had blackened me and my white eyeballs leapt out of my face when I managed to find a mirror.

During the trip, I talked with an Indian fellow for awhile and he told me about the terrible poverty in India. Dad, it was pathetic to see the rail gangs, and the women and children and old men working water buffalo and wading through water to cut long grass. We clicked past people living in old rotten thatched huts or flimsy skin tents. The monsoons must be a nightmare for them. I suppose they suffer horribly just to make it from one day to the next. And that Indian sun is so cruel. The man was telling me the government taxes the poor mercilessly and keeps them in their present state by its vicious levying.

The express got into Gorkhapur around 1.30 PM. Into a rickshaw with our backpacks and the box of Bibles. I feel badly watching these skinny young men pedal us and our gear from place to place but this is how things are done and all you can do is pay them well. Then into a minibus and off to the border, 100 kilometres distant. Still hot. But I have my window open full blast and I'm sticking my head out, just the way I loved it when I was a kid. At one brief stop we had fresh bananas (lots of bananas) and cold Coke from some enterprising villagers. The bananas only cost a rupee for nine or even more if you had time to bargain. A rupee is about 10 cents.

Through the palm trees and long fields of grasses and water, the cows and buffalo blocking the road, the bus horn screaming constantly. By 6.00 PM we are in Nautanwa, the Indian side of the border. Stamp, stamp on our visas. Walk. Nepalese side of the border. Stamp. Onto a bus for Butwal, first good-sized (no size at all, really) Nepalese town, 30 kilometres away. Stop, start. Stop, start. Two shepherds and their sheep get on. Stop, start. In 30 minutes, Butwal and the Butwal Technical Institute, recommended by our missionary friends in New Delhi. Three rupees for a single. Shower in the room. Bed. Fan. Heaven.

And here I am. Having a cold shower (no other kind once you've left Europe). I'm writing you and drying off. We're in low hills in Butwal. We shall try to get to Pokhara in the Himalayas tomorrow.

Had rice and curry tonight. Rice has been a staple food for all countries since Turkey. Iran had good rice (about half a pound or more per meal) but the best was in Afghanistan (pilau) with its bread cooked flat and round (nan). It's mostly brown rice in Afghan so that's better for you. Best rice meal yet was in Herst, a wonderful and fairly clean Afghan town. Lots of horses.

Tea or chi is also part of my diet now. Because it's boiled water and also because in this hot weather (still 100 Fahrenheit each day or more) it seems to be the only fluid that makes an attempt at defeating my thirst. I sweat so much! I think of ice drinks all day. I need cool air. Well, we and the big box are heading into the Himalayas. Now, I've got to sleep. Just plug in the fan (or you'll never breathe) and lie there like a rock. Goodnight, Dad.

Excuse my barely legible scrawl. Our pens keep drying in this tropical heat.

Now we are in Kathmandu. It was not easy to get here. In Butwal we got on an 11.30 AM express to Pokhara. The bus was so crowded and hot Curtis and I jumped on top with a bunch of young Nepalese guys. That box! I think the Bibles inside it must be multiplying like loaves and fishes, it seems to weigh more and grow larger every day. We had to lug it onto the roof with us and our gear to make sure it didn't disappear. Cramming it into trains and rickshaws is one thing. Having it bounce and slide around on the top of a twisting, turning bus is something else.

The sun was out, we had an unobstructed view of the huge, green Pokharan hills, as the bus whipped along we had a breeze. But all the hairpin mountain turns had us hanging onto the luggage rack and onto that big box that kept bashing into us and trying to swipe off our heads. There are actually two roads from Delhi to Kathmandu and we took the longer and more scenic route. The Pokharan area is big and green, full of gorges and white waterfalls. Everywhere is terraced land, thatched Chinese-style huts and people with Chinese features. Of course, once you get to Kathmandu you are only 100 kilometres from China, and there are many Chinese people in Nepal. Everest is right on the border. I handed out some of the lemons we'd bought and Curtis and I and our Nepalese roof-rack friends sucked on them while the land roared past. I was quite delighted at one stop when the young men made some sort of whistling sound and waved to a Nepalese beauty their own age dressed in traditional robes. She sailed on past, tall and slender, hair piled on top of her head, just as aloof as Everest itself.

But the road! After an hour and a half or so, the bus was less crowded and the driver ordered us back inside. The fun began. The road became full of ruts, boulders, and axle-breaking potholes. Half the time I was off my seat. Bam, bam, bam! I tried to hold the box of Bibles with my feet and it rammed my legs and ankles and gouged me. Six or seven hours later, about 8.30 PM, we bounced and smashed into Pokhara. I was so dizzy I could hardly eat at first. We stayed in Pokhara an extra day and rested. This morning we caught a bus to Kathmandu about 7.00 AM, another local express. About 21 rupees or $2.10. But the trip was delayed by a road accident. A truck ahead of us smashed into a young Nepalese man. It was grim. When Curtis and I walked up to see why traffic had halted on the one lane two-way road, we saw a white sheet over a body. It was raining and the sheet clung tightly to the body. There was blood seeping through the whiteness. It was the first time I'd seen the body of someone who had just been killed. It made me kind of nauseous to think that he had been alive and thinking a few minutes before. A huge ring of Nepalese stood and looked and argued and waited for the police. Evidently they considered the young man a bit crazy because he had gone to university. Someone from UNICEF finally drove out to get the police. It took over an hour. They pulled the body off the road and the traffic started moving again.

The road to Kathmandu from Pokhara was built by the Chinese in 1973 and it is smooth and straight. We got into Kathmandu about 4.00 PM and it was raining still. I had the address of the missionaries. They were at the Educational Book Exhibit, a bookstore quite famous in Nepal. Lots of good books but, in a way, you could say it was a front. Nepal doesn't really have religious freedom. Christians are forced to express their faith very discreetly. The store has many educational texts. It also has Bibles and Christian books. The government winks an eye.

Anyhow, it is a good store with good people behind it, and they welcomed us warmly. They took the big box off our hands which in itself is enough to make me love them. They were very excited about the Bibles. Once a month someone takes a load of Christian literature into the mountains, packed onto yaks, and they had not had Bibles for half a year. We were treated like heroes and shared their supper with them.

Kathmandu is an interesting city cupped by the tallest mountains in the world. The effect is even more dramatic because few of the buildings in Kathmandu are high by North American standards so you really do feel dwarfed. There are all kinds of pie shops amidst the red curls of the Buddhist temples and the bustle of the people and the saffron and scarlet robed monks. We were looking at the map tonight. We are over 12,000 miles from home. Half the world away. Sometimes you get homesick if you think too much about it.

It rained all day. I read and thought. Found wonderful books in the store. As if I didn't need more weight in my backpack, I stuffed in my new purchases: A Bible dictionary and commentary, *The Imitation of Christ* by Thomas a Kempis, *Go Down Moses* by Faulkner, *The Essential Hemingway, The Armies of the Night* by Mailer, *The Ring and the Book* by Browning, *The Wasteland and Other Poems* by Eliot, *Writings of Mahatma Gandhi, Penguin Collection of Contemporary Short Stories,* volumes one to six, *The Four Gospels (J.B. Phillips' translation), Cry, The Beloved Country* by Paton. Well, I don't have my big box to wrestle with anymore, so I should be able to handle my growing-ever-more-unwieldy backpack. I don't think I'll take too long to get through these. Perhaps I could let you know at the end of the letter what books I might like to have sent, books you might be able to find for me (plus a few of your own ideas).

Books do give me a feeling of comfort. I grew up around books. How good it used to be as a kid, still is, to fall asleep with a good book, then wake up early when there was no school and read more while the house was still silent. Or, as a kid, when you said "lights out", to go under the covers with a flashlight and keep on reading. I admit it was often touch and go. You almost caught me at it several times. If you'd only pulled back the covers while I was pretending to snore! All the paraphenalia you would have found!

I am sitting peacefully in the closed bookstore. They are holding an all-night time of prayer a few rooms away and you can hear them singing.

I join them off and on. But I wish to be alone just now. Curtis is nearby reading and it's okay, but I'd like it better if he went off by himself. I'm in my loner mood.

Wonder what's up for tomorrow? Wonder which country we'll head for next?

I can't believe it. We're on our way back to New Delhi with two boxes of books for the missionaries there. Two big wooden boxes and they each weigh a ton. The bookstore in Kathmandu asked us if we'd do them the favour. How could we refuse? Unbelievable. I feel like one of those mobile libraries that travel from town to town. And my pack alone is enough to break my back.

We left Kathmandu on Friday morning by truck. Cheap. We sat in the back with the rest of the people—and the two boxes. It was an open back with a skeleton wooden frame so you had something to hold onto if you wished to stand up during the ride—and invariably I did, because the truck had precious little shocks and sitting down meant kissing your kidneys goodbye. It was an all-day ride but the weather was warm and the scenery was hilly and green. It cost 60 cents and by five o'clock we were at the border. Got a rickshaw. Cycled us and the boxes from customs in Nepal to customs in India. He told us five rupees. When we got to our destination a few hundred yards from the border he demanded ten rupees. We paid it. Stayed at the Duncan Hospital in Raxaul, a Christian hospital suggested by our good friends at the Educational Book Exhibit in Kathmandu. Three rupees a night. They were outraged that we had paid ten rupees for the short rickshaw ride. But they do not have to manhandle those big boxes all the way to New Delhi.

We left Raxaul by bus in the morning. It was unbearably hot. We got moved from seat to seat by the driver and finally got stuffed in the back because of our long legs and those crazy boxes. The bus had no shocks, naturally. Thump, thump, WHUMP, thump. Curtis grouched, "They can spend a billion of Canadian aid on the atom bomb but they can't make decent roads!"

End up in Muzaffarpur about three or four in the afternoon. Raining. Rickshaw to train station. We asked the people around us how much the ride was worth. They said 50 paisa or six cents. We told the rickshaw peddler we'd give him a rupee each because of our heavy luggage. Got to the station and the peddler wanted two rupees each. I gave him one and Curtis gave him one. He began to get agitated. We grabbed our packs and boxes and lined up for tickets. The wickets opened at 4.30 PM. We were at the head of the line. Everyone else lined up beside us again. I went to get some chi. Came back and some guy was gesturing that Curtis was not really in the line and had to go back to the end (another long one). Same old story. We stayed where we were and told the man that he had lined up wrong. When the ticket booth opened, no one challenged us. We purchased our tickets and staggered away with our packs and boxes.

We asked a million people, including the police, what track the train to New Delhi left on. Track Three. We sat and waited, bought biscuits, drank tea. As invariably happens at public places in India, travellers are surrounded by the locals. Some just stare, for minutes on end, watching everything you do, every hand movement you make, every spot you happen to look towards. Others come and ask questions. Some engage you in a sophisticated conversation.

Then there are the kids. "Baksheesh! Baksheesh!" Free gift, free gift! Rupees are best but biscuits will do. Dad, there are so many starving beggars in India, so many cripples, and they all flock to white people like ants to honey. It's so depressing. How can I possibly give them enough food or enough change from my pockets? I wish I could heal them. An Indian Christian was telling me many people who have a lot of children may take one and put out his or her eyes, or cut off his legs, make him into a cripple, and send him out begging to bring in more money. Shades of *Oliver Twist,* some beggars even belong to organized groups, bring all their money in at the end of a day, and the head man takes his half, while they use the rest to buy food, everyone getting a small cut. If they don't get the money or food they do starve to death in the streets.

Our train came, we got into a car that was freshly opened and got seats for once, good ones too, window seats. We hadn't had time to get reservations so we just took unreserved second class, what used to be third class—cattle cars, if you will. Our car filled quickly. We sat back and breathed the damp night air. Two hours later we were throwing backpacks and boxes out the window—the boxes barely made it—and crawling out after them into the railyard of Bahali Junction. We were on the wrong train. The one we'd jumped onto in Muzaffarpur was heading for Calcutta. Asked more questions and found an empty train that was supposed to head for Patna soon, a stop on the way to Delhi. Got good seats again, our feet up on the boxes. The train was leaving at 2.00 AM. Soon our car filled but it was not really crowded. Before we reached Patna around 7.00 AM, Curtis and I were able to stretch out full-length and grab some sleep.

Got into Patna. Bought a few easy books, a thriller and one by Leon Uris. Indian bookstalls are far superior to our public stalls in North America. You can get Dickens and Hemingway and Waugh and Tolstoy, besides contemporaries such as Mailer and Solzhenitsyn. There are only a few sleazy sex books, whereas our stalls are full of blood, sex, and violence and pillow-prop romances. The train from Patna to Delhi (not an express, unfortunately) slid in and the crowds surged against its sides. There was no way we could get near an unreserved second class car. So we got into a reserved second class car along with a few others.

It was okay for the longest time. Then around noon we had a big stop and a huge Sikh roared aboard and began screaming at us: "OUT! OUT! OUT!" That's all he could say. We were in the middle of eating rice and curry from huge aluminum trays. Could we finish? "OUT! OUT!" How can we carry our packs and boxes and the food too? "OUT!OUT!" Where will we go? The cars are full. "Accommodation will be arranged for you!"

It was arranged, all right. We got out and never saw him again. We couldn't get in the unreserved cars, they were too full, the people locked the doors and wouldn't let us in. We told a skinny conductor. He said car 3947 was okay for us. We got in. The train moved out. The car was full of soldiers.

One of them said something to us—and our oversized boxes—about the car being reserved for military personnel. But the train was moving and there was nowhere to go so we remained in the car and had long amiable conversations with the soldiers. We had to stand. This lasted a couple of hours. Until the next big stop. On board came an enormous Sikh sergeant with an equally enormous turban. He was military police. He saw us. "OUT!" Out.

We demand a car. Conductors show us the unreserved cars. All right, get us in one. "It is not my responsibility." We hide in a reserved car. Before the train moves, we are found again and moved out. We are shown the unreserved cars, the bodies squeezed against the windows, the locked doors. "Well, get us in!" we snap at the conductors. "You will have to get the police for that," they respond. "Where are the police?" we ask. "I cannot say," one shrugs. The train starts moving. There is nothing else to do. We fling our boxes and packs into an open doorway. We fling our bodies after them. We sit up. The train picks up speed. We are in first class! And here we stay for three hours until we reach Kanpur, despite threats from the skinny conductor who comes aboard, says it is illegal for us to travel in a first class compartment, and that he will get the police. He never returns.

But at Kanpur at 9.00 PM we are firmly removed from the car. We make an attempt to get into an unreserved one. We consider crawling through the windows. We stick our heads into a car to check it out—bodies wall-to-wall, ceiling to floor, temperature about 212 degrees Fahrenheit. Lights blazing. No. We watch the train leave the station without us, another gleaming locomotive that looks like it just left the factory. It will arrive at Delhi at eight or nine in the morning.

There is another train at 10.15 PM on Track Four. We will try for that. We go and put down our packs and boxes and wait. People crowd around us, stare at us, ask us where we are from. Kids come up: "Baksheesh!" I say little, have no inclination to talk. My fingers, arms, and elbows are scraped and bleeding from dragging those crazy book boxes from car to car, train to train, through windows, through doors, through crowds of shouting and shoving people. I use some chlorinated water from my canteen to clean the cuts. It tastes like a swimming pool to drink the stuff, which is why I don't, but at least it's pure and can be used for wounds or for washing something. After awhile, everyone has disappeared. The station seems deserted. Curtis and I doze.

The rustling in the station wakes me. People are suddenly appearing from nowhere with massive suitcases and large bundles of clothing and cookware bound with ropes. Curtis and I put on our backpacks, tighten the hip belts, and heft the boxes into our arms. We are ready for business and have no intention of living out the rest of our lives in Kanpur. We will get on the next train to Delhi and stay on it.

I suppose if I were one of those train buffs who talk tracks and rail lines and wear tall striped engineer hats in their basements while their H&O diesels whistle up and down through papier mache mountains, I would have marvelled at the beautiful steam locomotive that snorted and panted and squealed into the station. It was as long and black and shining as a starlit summer's night. But it was an object of conquest. People swarmed towards it before it had even stopped. And Curtis and I assailed it with the rest, steam puffing up like white smoke about our legs.

I cut a swathe to one car, my box in front of me like a battering ram, only to find out the car is reserved. Curtis shouts. He's found room in an unreserved car! We pile in, ignoring the blows and pushes from other men and women already in the car. We gain the fortress and once we've battled our way inside, we are accepted and left alone. The doors are locked behind us and the windows shut. We tie our packs onto wall hooks with some rope, sit on the boxes, and try to stretch our legs a little. The train moves on. At the next stop the locked door is forced open from the outside and men fight their way in. I watch metal suitcases come flying through the windows that were not shut. People in the car are cursing and yelling and kicking hard at those who are trying to push through the door. Those who are forcing their way in do so with calmness and persistence, never striking back although blows are raining down upon their heads, coming and coming and coming until they are in. Then they too are accepted and the door is once again shut and locked behind them.

We are here because of the boxes. My face is black with dirt and soot. My white CANADA T-shirt is soiled grey and black. My hair is stiff like wire. The lights stay on. People sprawl over my legs. Suitcase corners dig into my sides. The air stinks. Curtis goes into the toilet to find some privacy and decides to lock himself in. All night as the train clatters through the Indian dark persons get up to use the bathroom. They hammer on the door. They yank and yank on the handle. They cry out. They plead. But, from inside the stainless steel closet, Curtis barks only two responses, "NO!" and "GO AWAY!" Towards dawn I sleep, twisted like a paper clip. I wake up and there is no sun. I see buildings. "What's this?" I manage to croak. A man glances at me: "Old Delhi."

The weather is cooler now, the monsoons are over. Hot and dry in the day, fresh and brisk in the night. Mornings are cool and delicious, a pleasure to walk or drive about in. All the fruit is pouring into Delhi from the countryside. Pineapples for 50 cents each. Bananas at two or three cents each. Big ones. Pomegranates. Mandarin oranges, practically seedless, 70 cents a dozen, beautiful Japanese Christmas taste. Coconuts, yellow apples, big red apples, little hard apples. It's cheap to live.

But nothing was better than delivering those two boxes to the mission. They welcomed us like long lost friends, ecstatic over the safe arrival of our cargo: "These books are so important for India!" I am glad those two boxes may yet change the world but now I am anxious to get out of Delhi as quickly as possible. I am sure that somewhere in the building, as I write, a cluster of missionaries are packing four large wooden boxes, readying them for a long, arduous journey, and somewhere, in a corridor between those boxes and Curtis and I, a missionary is walking, coming to ask us if, for the love of God, we will not take these boxes to Timbuctoo and save the world. So we will leave tonight, perhaps for Bombay, perhaps for Cairo or Athens or Jerusalem. We will wish our missionary friends farewell and be on our way before the thought of more boxes ever comes to their minds. We will begin with the night train to Lucknow and who knows where we will go from there? Nothing could be more tumultuous and unpredictable and wonderful as the Indian trains. I am sure there is an allegory in them Dante would have appreciated.

Dad, I will write again when I reach the end of the world.

DAUGHTER

It is the final summer before her birth. I do not mean her physical birth. She is five. But now the wildflowers grow below her knees. The daubings of oil that are her hands brim with the meadows. She is a moving field, moving under the moving swallows, and I regret forever that I was sometimes frustrated by the long days she remained at home and called to me while I tried to work in my studio. A fool, what a fool I was, but I saw the fool and I am not too late.

She sleeps in her bed without pyjamas this hot spring night, one night before her birth, three nights before the birth of summer. I touch her skin. It is warm. Hot mountain winds blow over the grasses and gardens and over our own home by the stream of melted snow. The stream is not high and muddy with the runoff from the snowfields in the mountains anymore. It is the colour of jade and you can see the young trout in those jade pools, see their bubbles and flickings as they rise to mosquitoes and flies. Sleep, daughter, as the stream runs to the sea. I did not notice your legs growing.

Now you will be at school all day. Others will spend more time with you than I. New friends will come, men will come, your own children, your own home, your own work, you will send me cards and come for visits and I will fall asleep in my favourite chair. None of it will be as wonderful as all the hours we live and breathe now.

Yesterday we went to the lake and picked wildflowers while our two dogs chased jackrabbits. They also grow old. I was only married to my Beautiful for three years when those two arrived at our door, puppies that ran as you run harvesting orange poppies and bluebells and sunflowers. They still run, but I age with them, and when they go on and away, I will no longer be the young man that raced with them through the northern evergreens, the stacked hillsides of lodgepole pine, the brooks and rivers and long unravelling summers. Be young with them, daughter. They can chase the rabbits, you can chase the flowers.

Life is crammed with much that does not fit. Let it break out like a pod of seeds. Like the cottonwoods with their June snow, spinning like white flies through the liquid sky, the moisture lazy in the air as great blue clouds spill over the mountains. I try to place a sheet over her but she kicks and twists so that it winds about her. I kiss her legs and her small flat stomach and her ribs. This is what heaven must be, a parent and a child loving each other and playing and hunting colour in a spring field and watching each other sleep.

Are there robins in heaven? I have made her and her brother Guardians of the Robin. There are two nests in our yard, one behind my studio in the fork of a cottonwood, the other in a chokecherry tree by the breakfast nook door, the door that is a sheet of glass. Sister and brother have to protect the nests from crows and cats, even children with long sticks who find amusement in destruction. Are these small blue eggs in heaven? What shall children do if there are no blue eggs the size of my thumb and the children are the Guardians of the Robin?

I lie beside her in the pale light. I carefully place an arm around her. My cool skin will be good for her. She murmurs something. When she was one her stomach was always upset and she cried constantly from the pain and would not gain any weight. We lived right in the mountains, among peaks and crags and glaciers and shifting light. The clouds were close. We brought her into our large bed to lie between us. She seemed happiest when I held her small feet in my hands and curled my long fingers over her toes. I had to sing. There was a whole medley, beginning with *Land of the Silver Birch,* carrying through *into My Paddle's Keen and Bright* and so down into *Shenandoah,* which is when she usually fell asleep. If not, there was *Amazing Grace.* She grew content and she slept, and my wife, my Beautiful, slept. But I lay in the dark singing to myself— or perhaps God hears this sort of singing too. I sing to my daughter again now, this last night, even though she is dreaming, because I remember the Shenandoah River and the lush valley around it and how the river winds back in upon itself, so old, so many twists and turns, so many loops, I saw it 30 years ago, how old is it now and what colours are its waters? For to my daughter and I, it bore us softly through the Virginia hills, and it is always the colour of sleep.

We parents have always asked how our children go so swiftly from a laughing infant to a running girl or to a boy who leaps, how is it done, where are we when this occurs? But I wonder something else, I wonder how she grew me? I recall a worse temper, quickly irritated by this and that of childish ways, a snapping voice that rose up out of me, a foolish anger that I regretted. But where is this anger now? She caught ahold of it. I do not know where she hid it. She raised me to be a father. I was not one before, not like the Shenandoah is a river. How did I go from this to that?

I have a whole summer before me. Yes, at dawn she will be six, but the school year begins in September, not in June. Tomorrow it is the presents and the cakes and the black and green soft drinks and the balloons and the streamers and the shouting and squeaking and wriggling of friends. There is a pink feather pen she wanted, the kind used in wedding ceremonies when the bride sits in a hush of white to write her name. There is a book on Peter Pan, one of her favourite stories. There is a horsedrawn carriage of pink and gold for her dolls. Roller blades for the warm summer streets. Music for her tape deck when she closes the door to her room and wants to draw alone or create a new world in secret. There are bright tops and bright pants. Small toy horses with a mare standing over her foal that is lying down, legs folded. Yellow and blue rubber dinghies with paddles for the stream behind the house. I know her Mother is buying her fingernail polish.

Let the party begin at sunrise then. But I still have the summer, all its heat and sudden storms, the swirling of dandelion fluff and the brilliance of meadowlarks. And beyond that? I am still the father she asked me to become. I do not have to stop praying for her or hugging her or stop working in my studio hoping to hear her call the new name she offered me. I would rather stay in the meadow and see the jackrabbits spring grey and white from a dry yellow bush or watch red butterflies flicker around her fingers. But they will not let me remain in those fields. And cradling her head and shoulders in my arm here on cotton sheets printed with daisies they will not let me stay. Yet the father has not been growing for six years for nothing. It is my birth tomorrow too. Once I was just another man who wrote stories and preached sermons. Now we belong to each other. Her birthday is also mine. This matter is not settled in six years or in 60 years or in 600,000 years. It is unstoppable. Time may age the body but it only ripens the soul.

I lie here in the new dark and she is unaware of me. Or maybe in that part of her that knew my presence while she floated in the womb, in that place she knows I am lying here counting the stars. I should rise and snip a yellow blossom from her brother's rose bush or pluck a cluster of pink flowers from her honeysuckle. She loves lilac, I ought to fill her room with that before the coming of the sun. There is so much I should be up and doing. In time I will go in where my Beautiful rests. For now it is a night like the night before our daughter was born.

Death and suffering will come. Cold and sharpness. Yet the colours will be here too. And the love. But eventually silence will arrive and pass through our doorposts.

Now I will tuck the quilt of daisies up to your chin. Whisper, the night. Let her have a few more hours of innocence. Let the sun paint her since she herself loves to paint. I will know her as another person at day-break.

CHAPTER

THE STATIONS
OF THE CROSS

There was a forest beside the house and when he was a boy he went to it. They took the forest away but he had enough of it in his head to keep it. So in his dreams he continued to walk among the trees and down by the marsh where the Canada Geese gathered in the spring and in the fall. He would sit down under an oak and write in a large red notebook. These were his stories. He could hardly remember a time when he was not writing them. When God came through the forest and sat down beside him under the oak and told the boy stories of earth, wind, and fire, it only seemed natural to the boy to believe these stories and to love them and the one who told them. There was no indication that the boy's own stories should stop. He continued to set them down in his red notebook, though now God's stories interlaced with the boy's like ivy curling green through a white and sturdy lattice.

In time, when he was thirteen, Alexander felt a need to share his stories and he sent one to a magazine that was printed and sold to thousands of churches. It was a great day when a letter came back in the mail and not the manuscript. They would publish the story in the new year and they wanted a photograph of him. He received a cheque for 25 dollars—it felt like 25,000 dollars to him. His pen continued to scratch words roughly across pages, racing to keep up with his imagination, so that the stories were indecipherable to anyone but him.

Copies of the published story arrived in the mail and he tore the manila envelope open in a powerful joy. Immediately he was delighted with the colour picture of his protagonist walking under the lamplight of a dark street. There was his own photograph and it also looked well. Then he read the story. Cold slammed against his heart and his mind. Anger and pain came gouging up from his stomach on clawed feet and pierced the trunk of his being. How could they do this? They had changed his story. He had struggled in his notebook not to write a sermon or a religious tract but a real story, full of a boy's doubts about God and how the boy had wrestled his way to a place of faith. But they had disembowelled his tale and reduced it to a formula where the boy's doubts were resolved in half the time and half the space, only one paragraph given over to an agonized spirit. The metaphors and similes were gone, the finely crafted sentences, the minute detail. The poetry and the art were shredded. It was no longer the creation of his hands, it was no longer his brain that wound around the letters, it was without flesh or spirit, and the image stabbed him of a fish skeleton on a beach, sunk in sand and dried weed, pricking with bones. They reserved the right to edit. How could they alter his genesis so that it was reduced to a darkness on the face of the deep? Rage frothed through him for days like whitewater bolting through a gap. He burned the story, nodded politely when people at church praised him for being published in the magazine, and cashed the cheque to buy more notebooks and more pens, in defiance, going to the forest his mind created and writing his stories there. He never sent any to the magazine again.

His pastor waved the boy's frustration off: "Don't waste your time. You need to train as a pastor or a missionary. That's where God wants you." He began to write less. A few summers later he joined a mission team in Italy, taking Christian books door to door in Caserta and Assisi and small towns on hills full of old walls and old women wrapped in black. One evening the team was resting at a farmhouse where every window was an oil painting ripe with colours and with growing things and the gold slanting sun, and in a surge Alexander went to one of the adult leaders and said he hoped to be a writer for God, that perhaps one day his books would be translated into the warm yellows and reds of Italian and taken to houses where a man had no hope, a woman had no God. The leader snorted, "I don't know why you guys waste your time thinking about that kind of stuff. You can write when you're old. Do the things that matter now. Tell people about God. If the Lord wants you to spend the rest of your life as a foot soldier going door to door with tracts, then be happy doing that because it's what God wants." The boy retreated in dismay to a window that overlooked a green hill that throbbed with bees and he thought of Michaelangelo and Da Vinci and he went to the forest in his mind and sat there until God came and showed him an ochre flower he had never seen.

When he returned to his church from Italy some people were angry with him and argued that he should have gone overseas with a mission team from their own denomination. When an offering was taken up to defray his summer travel expenses 200 people placed 32 dollars in the offering plate. Later in the week, at a spiritual retreat hosted by the church, an adult leader approached Alexander and his friend and asked them what they did for work.

"I write," said Alexander.

"I lay tiles," said his friend.

"Ah, now, there's a man's job," responded the leader. "I used to lay tiles and linoleum and carpet myself. I think God gets close to those of us who do manual labour like he did, don't you?"

The pastor called Alexander into his office one afternoon in September.

"What are your plans?" he asked the boy.

"I'm going to take some classes in creative writing at a community college."

The pastor grimaced. "You can't help anyone doing that. You need to be a pastor. What difference is it going to make if you write a story or not? Where is the Spirit of God in that? It just takes you away from God. All the arts do that. Unless you are going to write a tract or paint a picture of a Bible story or play a hymn on the piano. Quit shutting God out, Alexander. Let him be Lord of your life and let the stories go."

Alexander stumbled into his twenties. He went to the college and wrote more stories and even some poetry but he felt dirty. He was a shadow on the road, a thin sharp splinter, he had turned his back on God. The pressure would build inside him, inside his mind and his spirit, and he would fling the stories and the notebooks away and come wholeheartedly to church, free of the writing, pure, singing hymns, reading the Bible, talking the talk of the people of God. Until the fires would rise again and he must take up his pen. But since he could not do that and be close to God, he came to church less and less, burying himself in his apartment with his novels and his red notebooks that swarmed with incomprehensible writing.

The years tripped back and forth across his body and the men and women and children he met sparkled in his mind like rough gemstones. He went to seminary and preached good sermons, fine sermons, but at night and in the summer he wrote stories that he showed no one. He loved

God so he dressed in a three-piece suit and knotted a dark tie and climbed into wooden pulpits and he spoke and he felt clean. But not in his dreams. One night he ran through the streets and past the glittering dark buildings of his mind, spraying bullets from a machine gun and killing, finally trapping one of his quarry who turned on him, and was him, and who fired at Alexander's heart. Alexander felt the bullet go in and the shock and the slippery blood. The angry person that was himself snapped at Alexander: "What did you expect? You're destroying us. You're destroying yourself. We'll kill you to stop it."

Awake, Alexander peeled off the grey suit and hung it in a far corner of the closet. He married a woman among seashells and seahorses and breaking combers. He was determined to write again, he stormed into the green waves shouting for God. He thought and wrote and typed but somehow he wound up a pastor in a church again. They tore at him with their mouths as he preached and counselled but he would not let them, anyone, stop the stories this time. He crafted them and read them from the pulpit until the day came when he fled from the church once more, his bride with him.

He sat down in the tall grasses under the oak tree, grasses that could slit your hands wide open if you tugged at them in the wrong way, and he wrote a longer story, a novel, and since the Christians did not seem to want it, men and women who did not care much for God took it and published it. Now his life was filled with writing. He spoke on television about his book, he spoke on the radio, at bookstores, at universities, at museums. Sometimes people came to listen, sometimes they did not. When a second book was written and launched in his hometown, friends and well-wishers laughing and eating cheese and sipping wine, and he autographing, his wife sat next to him on the staircase once they had returned home and he was bleak, a cold December night in a cold December night. Was this all? A wine and cheese party, book sales, signatures, talk shows and promotional tours? There was no reason to write anymore. There was nothing to say. There was no God. His wife twisted her fingers through his hands: "It is possible to be both. To be an artist and a believer."

"That is not what they say, Charlie. Society will say I am too Christian. The churches will say I am not Christian enough."

"They know nothing about it, in the church or out of it. Who gives the lion its voice? Who gives the hawk its flight? Who tells the prophet to speak?"

"Either I write and I am cut off from God. Or I don't write and I am close to God."

"Who insists on that dichotomy?"

"It's what I've always been told."

"You don't even believe it."

"Not really. But that's how it seems to work out in my life."

Alexander had spent three years writing. His forest was leafless and God did not come to him there. So he went to a church again and he was a pastor and for five years he scarcely wrote. He became ill and could not rise from his bed. He took a leave of absence. Slowly he walked up hills near his house, trying to build up his strength. In the evenings he sat with Charlie and watched the stars float on top of the sea.

"I would write again but I make no money at it," he said.

"Write anyway. I don't want to go back to the churches. They eat us alive. God can give us something else."

"What would that be?"

"I don't care."

"There's nothing else. I'm trapped."

"We're not trapped. Write your stories."

"That magazine wants me to write six a year now."

"When did they tell you that?"

"Last week."

"You never told me. That's wonderful."

"There's no money in it."

"We'll find the money we need. I want you a living, breathing man. A corpse is of no benefit to me."

"If I die you get a big insurance payout."

"There is that. But no one to spend it with."

"Someone will turn up."

"Alex, if God can write, so can you, and you can share the same table in the same library. Writing does not have to take you away from him. I doubt it ever has."

"What would it be like to swim forever in the sea down there and never get cold, never get tired? That would be a great thing. And always night and always stars and everything soft."

Alexander wrote and made no money. So he preached and made a living. Sometimes he was asked to speak at writers' conferences, sometimes at other churches because of his stories. Sometimes he shared a few of his stories with his own church but few of the people seemed interested. Sermons and Bible studies and counselling and potlucks were the thing. He read in several Christian magazines how the Christians who wrote historical romances were making big money. "So much so," wrote one columnist, "that Stephen King ought to think hard about becoming a believer and making his fortune writing for the Christian market." One Christian author confessed in an article, "I started out trying to write good stories about real people and real life. But I couldn't get picked up by the Christian publishing houses. I couldn't break into the secular market either. So I gave it up. I had to make a living. I've turned to the romances and now I'm doing well, thank God."

Alexander knew the romance writers were doing well. He could see that everytime he walked into a Christian bookstore. Rack after rack of the stuff. There was nothing else in the fiction section except westerns and end-of-the-world scenarios and a few supernatural thrillers. Why did Christians have such a problem writing about real life? Why couldn't they write books where Christians were ugly or short-tempered or where they struggled with their faith or experienced tragedies or watched their prayers drop lifeless to the ground? Why was it all dolls and daffodils or dark and stormy nights with demons on the wing? Why was all the fiction working off of the same script? Why were the characters cut out of cardboard? Why were Christians afraid of honesty? Why did they prefer illusion?

"No," said Charlie. "Thousands of people read your stories. Some are Christians and some aren't. Not everyone wants the romances and the thrillers. A lot may dip in but they don't want that stuff for a steady diet. It would be like eating bowlfuls of white sugar for all your meals. You have an audience. People are listening. Keep writing."

"And keep preaching."

"The two aren't mutually exclusive. No matter what Pastor Donut said when you were a kid."

"I never told you about the couple that farmed. They gave me a note when I came back from Italy and everyone was hassling me about being a writer."

"What did they say?"

"They were older, in their 70's, I guess they'd be dead now, but they were way beyond everyone else. They wrote that they'd noticed that everytime some young person got excited about God in the church everyone automatically pointed them towards seminary or the mission field. They felt that was wrong. I wanted to be a writer, didn't I? I should go ahead and be one and God would bless it."

"And you didn't believe them?"

"Everyone else was on the other side."

"Do you wish you'd never done the seminary thing now? All the preaching? All the churches?"

"You know what it's been like, Charlie. An artist trying to be a pastor. The churches don't want an artist saying things in a creative way. They want someone to say the same things over and over in a predictable fashion. They want to go home feeling the world is a safe and secure place. They don't want to be challenged and they certainly don't want to hear about Job or Lamentations or the Garden of Gesthemane."

"Those things aren't the whole story anyway."

"No. But they're a big part of it. People don't want God's story anymore."

"If you are going to keep getting drained by this Mary Poppins generation of churchgoers it would be better if you'd wait until an east wind comes and blows them all away. Write. There will always be preachers, good ones too. But the churches don't have many good writers to help them. I can be crass about it: One of your sermons reaches a hundred people, a published story reaches ten thousand or more in that magazine. So where do you think you should be spending your time?"

"It's been bad in the churches, Charlie. But it's also true that it's helped my writing. I used to have all kinds of ideas and plots and I'd work them out but the characters were paper thin. They weren't real. Because I'm a pastor I've worked with all the real people and all their real personalities and real problems. It's made my stories flesh and blood, not just spirit."

"But I've watched it killing you too. The churches are rejecting creation, Alex. They're rejecting thought and mind. They've been rejecting the imagination for the past two hundred years. You can't keep putting yourself in harm's way. Let's go underground. I'll play the flute and you write."

"I love God so I end up in pulpits."

"You can love God and end up in print too."

"There's no money in the writing."

"Alex! I'm sick of it! Is that the only reason you preach? A paycheque?"

"No. I've done a lot of pulpit time without a paycheque."

"Why do you pastor?"

"You said there were hardly any good writers. We need honest pastors too."

"You don't have to be everything."

"And God loves writers just as much, right?"

"He's one himself, isn't he?"

By the time he was 40 Alexander was pastoring his fifth church. Some had been small, some large, some just church plants starting from scratch. One day a week he wrote his stories. He wanted more time. But pastoring didn't offer anymore time. There was too much to do. Not so much the preaching and teaching. That only took up maybe a quarter of the time. The rest of it was basically management—people, letters, plans, phone calls, e-mails. A pastor was a director unless the church was big enough to have several pastors for different responsibilities. Then maybe one person could concentrate on the preaching and teaching. But how many pastors had that option? Most were a jack of all trades. Maybe a certain kind of person loved that. In fact, Alexander could remember a crusty old minister at the seminary praising God for the wonderful diversity of the pastorate. Alexander wished he could feel that way about it. But after twenty years he didn't feel like he had done very much of the things he loved most—speaking and writing.

Sunday morning and Wednesday night were scarcely enough to satisfy his love of teaching and preaching and one Friday a week was hardly enough time to write half a chapter in a novel or one portion of a very short story. Most of his time and energy were taken up with the sort of chores that had to be done but which did little to inspire him. He often daydreamed about spending 60% of his work on preaching and reading and writing and 40% on the management side. But these were dreams that flew from his grasp like swallows. Maybe in some places it was happening for some pastors. Maybe in other ages it had been commonplace for pastors to do more writing and teaching. Maybe in generations to come it would return and the pastor would be sought after as a wise man again instead of as a CEO. But for now it was what it was.

Alexander did not hate the people. He loved them most of the time. But it broke his heart to plan prayer meetings people ignored or Bible studies people bypassed on the way to the video store. He was himself to a certain extent, but not all of himself, and it hurt to realize people preferred a bland pastor to a creative one, even when he suppressed so much. It would give him immeasurably more peace, perhaps, to write church and God off as a job to be borne until his free time rolled around each week when he could really live. But it also might bring him very quickly into the hell of a life that was neither fish nor fowl, an existence that was simply containment, part of his life locked in a vault utterly isolated from another part. He doubted he could remain human and live that way. Even less than he could serve as pastor to a congregation caught up · in the glitz of their Christian romance that he had better not burst the bubble of or let slip to the harsh ground their brittle glass slipper. So he continued to live on a street somewhere between heaven and hell and he spoke and taught when he could, writing when he must, when the fires of creation were sure to engulf him. He suffered but he would not cross the line and declare the church a job, a necessary drudgery. He would only call it a cross, a burial, and exist in the hope of a resurrection.

At 45 he was tired, so tired he imagined he might be 75 and pushing 80. He caught himself committing the unpardonable sin, dreaming about retirement when he would finally do all the things he wanted, not just things for himself but the fine and exhilarating things he had always wanted to do for God. He had never wanted to live that way or think that way, marking time, slumbering through thirty or forty years until he could really come to life, but it was happening and, he knew, not just to him, but to millions of others who had sworn at 25 they would never stick at something that ate them up, believing they'd be strong enough at 65 to enjoy a sharp, sweet ending to a difficult life. Jesus had said he'd come to give people life to the full. What had happened? Alexander had experienced a fullness once, a long time ago, before the churches he had ministered at in this odd generation. Or perhaps not so odd. Look at Moses' life or Paul's life. And they never retired. Alexander closed the door to his study on Fridays and wrote out of his pain and his despair but also out of his tenacity and his faith and his love for God and all that God had made and redeemed.

"You can step out anytime," Charlie insisted.

"No, I can't."

"I won't stay married to a corpse."

"Is that what I am?"

"Some days, a lot of days, that's exactly what you're like."

"I have to do it this way for now."

"Why? How do you know the world isn't dying right now because there aren't enough good storytellers? How do you know the churches aren't dying because not enough good writers are writing? And there you sit, dying yourself, and you could be part of the cure but you won't write more than a few pages once or twice a month, you won't use the gift and it's destroying you, it's destroying the earth. You're playing it safe."

"Being a pastor is playing it safe?"

"For you it is. It's slavery but you prefer it to the fears that come with freedom. Who wants the pillar of fire in the wilderness when you can have the comfort of a predictable suffering in a slave camp? I won't take another twenty years of this, Alexander."

"Just a day at a time. Then I'll be able to do the writing."

"What if you die at 50?"

"Then I die."

"And when do we start living? When I'm 90? You want me to put love and life on hold till then? Are you telling me that's what God wants?"

"No."

"Then let's go and do something we really believe in."

"We believe in the church."

"Not in these kinds of churches. God has an infinite variety of churches. Let's find one that loves him and loves the act of creation."

"Where?"

"Who knows? Let's have something called faith and just launch out, have an exodus. Tonight."

"I'm too tired to play Moses tonight."

"You're always tired. You'll be tired tomorrow night too and next week. But I'm tired too, Alexander. I'm very tired."

She left him in July, the same month they'd been married fifteen years before. He didn't know where she'd gone to and her parents and friends weren't telling. Since it was officially only a separation, Alexander's denomination kept him on for awhile, but after eight months they let him go and the church reluctantly agreed. Alexander moved back to his home city and got a job driving a cab. In this year of many things came one more thing. His mother and father died three weeks apart and what had been the family home for fifty years, the home they'd all grown up in, had to be cleared out and sold.

Everything was there. Not just the clothing his mother and father had worn or the books, the thousands of books they had read that spilled over into virtually every room that had shelves. There were drawings and prints his brother Brian, the professor of art, had left behind 30 years before, and the two brothers found them in the basement curled and glued with grey dust. Alexander found old poems he had written, old photographs, a copy of his disembowelled first story. Each drawer or cupboard seemed to yield another item forgotten years before in the hurry of growing up and the sudden departure from home for work or university.

The process was both exhilarating and emotional. Their minds told them a radio ought to be playing in every room, that Dad's bass ought to suddenly boom out with *Red Sails in the Sunset* or *Beautiful Dreamer* or *Let Me Call You Sweetheart,* that Mom ought to be shouting out as she tried to watch Wheel of Fortune or Dallas while Dad seized her legs and dug in his fingers and tickled her feet. But there was nothing. No one called "Alex!" or "Brian!" No one spoke to them.

One afternoon Alexander worked the house alone while Brian finished up some work at the university. The house he had been a young boy in suddenly became cold and strange as he sorted through books and papers. He felt an awful end to all things secure and safe. Charlie was gone, his mother and father were gone, the ministry of a pastor was gone, soon the house he and his brother had played in and become artists in would be sold. There was a crushing and a collapse throughout his entire head and body. He fled from the house to the green fields across the street.

This was where the forest had stood when he was four years old. There had been a cocker spaniel in the family then who often walked over to the woods with him. The dog chased after jackrabbits fruitlessly, Alexander clinging to the leash even after he had fallen and the spaniel was dragging him through the trees and brush. There had been curling trails, a broken down Model A Ford, deer, the marsh, squirrels and chipmunks and fox. Until the day of the yellow bulldozers that tore up the trees by the roots and piled them in huge pyres which other men doused with gasoline and lit. The fires burned and smoked for days. The ground was torn and soft with exposed brown soil for half a mile in each direction. He had walked through the smoking ruins as if he was walking through a war. The roots struck into the air scorched and black.

Now it was rows of lights for aircraft approaching the southern runway, and acres of grass, a few ball diamonds, a scattering of trees spared from the carnage of long ago. As Alexander walked over the fields his mind opened and stories came tumbling through him. He came to a scrub oak and sat back against it. He had no pen or paper. But he let his mind play and hoped he would be able to recall the gist of it later.

When the sun was low he returned to the house. Brian was sitting on the front steps looking a bit worried. Alexander sat beside him.

"Where were you?" asked Brian.

"Over in the forest."

"The forest?"

"Where it used to be."

"Oh, yeah." Brian passed him some bottled water. "How many books do you think there are?"

"About five thousand."

"Do you think Dad read them all?"

"No. Half of them don't even look as if they've been opened. But he always liked books. Remember his war diary? Even back then he was buying them like crazy with the Heinkels dropping bombs over his head."

"Yeah." Brian laughed. "What about you, old man? How's your war?"

"I'll make it."

"Charlie coming back?"

"No."

"What about your preaching?"

"Some churches won't let you be a minister once you're divorced."

"That sounds stupid. Half the people in the world are divorced. Half the people in your pews. Who can understand their pain? Reverend Once In A Lifetime?"

"They want their pastors to be role models."

"What? They think life is like the Boy Scouts? No one is going to be inspired by Mister Perfect."

"It's the way it is."

"So you're going to drive a cab the rest of your life?"

"Just for a while."

"What about your writing?"

"I don't know. There was never enough time."

"There's time now."

"I still have to pay the rent."

"You always worried about money, you know that?"

"Never had much of it."

"What would you do if you did have it?"

"I don't have it."

"If you did."

"If I really had it? Go south for a year or two and empty my brain onto paper. I'd buy a thousand roller ball pens and write until everyone of them went dry. I'd write until the end of my life."

"South where?"

"Arizona. New Mexico. Southern California. The Baja. Hot and dry and plenty of sun. I'd write and let the desert read over my shoulder."

"You crazy Christians and your deserts. Okay, I absolve you. We'll finish the house and then you can go."

"Thank you, Father O'Brian."

"I'll get the money for you, my son, but you have to truly go."

"Aye, I promise I shall go, Father. Santa Fe first. Then Tuscon. I'll lose myself in a grotto."

"I have your word on it, my child?"

"Aye, my word, Father."

"Spit in your hand and shake on it."

"What?"

They both laughed. Brian drained his bottle and looked over at the fields golding in the summer sunset.

"We used to play football there after the trees were gone," he said. "I swear tackle football was a lot easier on the body than touch. We had a good place to grow up. Even the city buses didn't run up this far for years."

"It was good."

"Now you have to write about it. I'll make a watercolour of the house. You write the stories."

"Sure."

"You have to go, you know."

"Go where?"

"Go where you promised."

"Are we into that Father O'Brian stuff again?"

"There was a will, Alex. You never asked me about it."

"I never thought about it."

"You'll be able to go wherever you want. I'm serious. I want you to get out of here. Get out of this country, get away from this house and all the crazy pastor rules and the crazy churches, get away from me and that taxi cab. Just take your pen and your paper and go. Walk across those fields and get into one of those planes. I'd make you do it now but the house is too much for any one man."

"All right, Brian. I'm tired enough these days to let you talk me into anything."

"You say "all right" but if you don't mind I'll walk you up to your seat on the plane to make sure. Anyway. We've been on our duffs long enough. Let's get back to the pit. And I'll tell you something."

"What now?"

"Maybe you'll get to preach again. Maybe you'll one day let God put the two of them together in your head. The poet and the pastor. You want to hear something Dad told me? It was when Mom and him were visiting you a few years ago and they came to one of your services. Dad said when you got up to preach he could see everyone lean forward towards you. He could feel them hanging on your words. I think the writer and the preacher ought to come together like they did in Donne and Hopkins."

Alexander followed Brian back into the house and they sorted books until two in the morning. A month later the house was on the market and Brian kept his promise to escort Alexander as far as airport security would let him. Alexander stepped out into the summer cauldron of Phoenix. The sun actually hurt him, it cut right through his skin and twisted the blade. He stayed in the city a few days and then got on a bus. South and west of Tuscon he found a place he liked called San Miguel.

He would rise early to sit on the small patio of a rented two bedroom rancher with red Spanish roof tiles and walls painted a white that made his eyes and teeth ache. The sun rarely failed him. His paper glistening as if in a transfiguration, he wrote every morning from five until noon. Then he walked with the desert blazing over and under and around him. The town thought he was crazy, loco, that they'd pick his body up out of the sands. But they didn't know how many years he had waited to come back to life and they had no idea how tenacious that life was. After three years he was one of them. He never left San Miguel. Sometimes he might go away for a few months and write in Madera Canyon or hole up near the Dragoon Mountains and Cochise's stronghold. He knew the brave chief's story and admired him and wanted the same land and winds and vistas to carve him. Between San Miguel and Madera Canyon and Cochise he learned to pray again, he learned to worship, and Christ came as close to him as the blood that ran in and out of his heart.

A church began in his house and it stayed there. When they had more than 30 people another family started a sister church. This eventually spread to about 12 houses. Once a month they gathered in the desert and spent the whole day together, singing and talking and sharing their picnic lunches, and the children raced the Spirit of God over the sands.

Alexander kept on writing and preaching and walking and in the evenings he read and wondered under the enormous desert sky. Around the time he turned 67 he felt complete but God did not take him so he continued both to live and to anticipate life. Many of his stories and books were published and many were not. The royalties were meagre but they were enough to buy groceries and the legacy had dealt with his mortgage years before. He sensed the words he wrote were strong and good, that he was writing better than he had ever written, that he wrote better every year. And then one morning of fire and sun he left his manuscripts stacked neatly on his writing table and a note explaining he was going to his grotto and would probably stay there a long, long time, maybe until it was all over. San Miguel fretted and grieved but he did not come back.

Ten years after his disappearance his published writings were "discovered". Gaining enormous popularity, his works were translated into 14 languages, won numerous awards, and made Alexander something of a household name. The Christians began to claim him as one of their own and to market him. He was not around to protest. Perhaps he was still alive in his grotto but did not know or did not care. Friends from San Miguel often travelled into the desert south and east, even into Mexico, looking for the cave, asking questions, but Alexander had become invisible. No one had seen him or ever heard of such a man. What the desert knew it kept in the sort of silence only a desert or a hermit can keep. And what became of his body, God only knows.

CHAPTER *12*

THE HEART OF THE MOUNTAIN

April 6

Spring can bring a kind of madness. A fast melt is an explosion not only in the world around but in the world within. Everything accelerates. Everything is in a great hurry. It is a liberation and sometimes you need to go somewhere with all your energy, you need to circumnavigate the globe in a sailing vessel, or learn how to duel with sabres, or run a marathon through high, dry Apache desert. This year Toby wants to climb mountains.

I haven't mentioned Toby before in any of my diaries or journals. I'm the pastor, he's the professor of New Testament Greek, a short black-haired sparkplug of a man who is always reading Homer or Luke in the original. Both of us have requested leaves of absence without pay, which only confirms our madness to most. Toby snorts when colleagues arch an eyebrow at his plans to travel halfway around the world in order to express his freedom in Christ. He is fond of tirades and soliloquies and I offer a conflation of several of his best, improvised on the spot when confronted with the incarnate mediocrity of a hefty portion of contemporary Christianity:

Christianity ought to be like a polar expedition. Or an ascent of K2. Or all sails set and roaring down upon the Spanish Main to battle corsairs, firing broadsides and boarding ships with pistol and cutlass amidst great gouts of flame and smoke. Maybe it was like that in Paul's day or

Athanasius' day. But now Christianity has become big business and churches are nothing more than retail outlets. BIG EVENT AT OUR CHURCH! SHOP HERE! COME TO OUR CHURCH! WE'VE GOT IT ALL! BIGGER! BRIGHTER! BOLDER! BETTER! It makes me want to puke. Money-grubbing, attention-grasping little churches and all the pastry-faced, fat-bellied pastors. They want their DMINs so people have to call them doctor, CEOs of their department store chains of faith. free enterprise Christianity and all its sales figures and profits and number crunching. I swear to God, I'm sick of it. I'm sick of having a hand in training these morons and turning them loose so they can create even more of this shopping mall Christianity. I tell you, it was meant to be the Battle of Trafalgar or Uxbridge's charge of the heavy cavalry at Waterloo. Or Gypsy Moth circles the globe. What have we made it into? A very careful bore. Even when we call it a revival or a renewal we make it into a sales event: "We've got it! This is the place to come and shop! It's incredible what we have going on here today! Come on down!" We trivialize everything and by doing that we make everything dull and lacklustre and predictable. There's no glory, no honour, no code, no adventure. God Almighty, I will take on Everest or die!

Toby's tirades and ventings of spleen are always entertaining and highly quotable. And they always end with a definite plan. In this case, not a polar expedition or hunting down pirates in the Caribbean, but going to Everest, not as part of a big expedition team, but just getting up there and seeing it and maybe going up a mountain near it, one we would be allowed to tackle without a lot of money or red tape or ropes or ice axes or oxygen. I step down from the pulpit in May, the same time Toby finishes his classes and his grading.

August 2

May was already too late for us to get to Nepal for the spring trekking. So we've planned and organized and hiked in the Rockies all summer. Now we're about to bid our wives and families goodbye as if we're heading off to war. We fly to India in little more than a month, then we'll take trains and buses into the Himalayas. We expect to arrive in Kathmandu by the end of September.

September 20

We arrived in New Delhi on the 16th and I thought we'd have left India by now for Nepal. We got our visas and were ready to board a train for the border when Toby took violently ill. We thought it might be hepatitis but he was checked over at the All India Medical Institute and it turned out just to be a stomach ailment due to the radical change in diet. We are staying at a Christian mission now. They put Toby in a separate room and stuck a fan by his feet. I'm in another room with a Canadian from Ontario and an American from Kansas and a few young Indian men. We also have a fan. If there wasn't a fan, you would hardly ever get to sleep because the air is so close at night. When we first arrived in Delhi we used a campsite so we could test our tent. The monsoons drenched us. Then the heat would come and boil us. At night, sleeping in the tent was like sleeping in a steambath. The tent stood up to the test better than we did.

The country has changed, the climate has changed, the religion has changed, and the food that has twisted Toby's stomach into knots is dif-ferent. Nothing is like home. We ate a lot of rice with hot chillies and curries when we first arrived. It is tasty but it is hot. About the best food, or drink they have in India is what is called a *lassie,* a milkshake composed of fresh yogurt, a little water, sugar, and chopped ice. It's very cold, foamy, and delicious.

The people are quite attractive. The Sikhs are handsome, the men have very fine features. The girls and women themselves are beautiful in their colourful and diaphanous saris. All this pleasantness doesn't relieve the heat, however. It's at least 100 degrees Fahrenheit every day (our Indian friends call it coolish). But Toby has his fan and his juice and water, even an Indian nurse who is a Christian to check on him. I expect Horatio Nelson to survive. I can't imagine God letting him die before he even gets a chance to board HMS Victory and set sail for Cape Trafalgar.

September 26

We arrived in Kathmandu today. It is a quaint city of simple buildings, further humbled by the tallest mountains in the world which ring it like a palisade constructed of great white speartips. The effect on me was a mixture of enthralment and fright. I might be content to sit in Kathmandu and eat its famous pies and gaze at God from a distance if it were not for Toby.

We left New Delhi on the 22nd. Toby is well and regaining his strength. The nurse got him re-examined by the Chief Medical Officer at the nearby All India Medical Institute. This confirmed that it had only been some sort of upper stomach ailment. So we took trains to the border and then Nepalese buses into Kathmandu. Not the most pleasant journey as the roads were bad. I was afraid the bouncing and banging might cause Toby a relapse but he held up well.

The Everest trek may be begun in Kathmandu, in which case it would be 150 miles to Namche Bazar, a big Sherpa town, and then another 30 miles to Edmund Hillary's 1953 base camp. But Toby is impatient to get right up into the mountains while the fall weather is in our favour, so we will fly into Lukla, which is only 15 miles below Namche Bazar. We'll need to take this part of the trek very slowly due to the dangers of altitude sickness. They say five days from Lukla to Base Camp. We shall take eight to ten days. One Sherpa porter at 15 rupees a day and he finds his own food. Food can be obtained from villages almost right up to Base Camp at 18,000 feet. Rice and lentils. Yogurt. With our food supplements I'm sure we will do well. The entire trek from Lukla to Base Camp, back to Lukla and Kathmandu, should take us about three weeks. Luck we don't need. Prayer could help.

September 29

There is a good chance we will meet the members of the British Everest Expedition who just scaled the peak's south-west face. According to Toby's books, Chris Bonnington attempted the same climb, which is Everest's hardest approach, in 1973. It had never been done before and Bonnington didn't succeed then either. The expedition was defeated and an Australian team member was killed in an ice-fall. But this time Chris has done it and he is still up there, along with Doug Scott and the rest of the expedition. If we time our trek right, we shall meet them on their way down, perhaps at Base Camp.

We obtained our trekking permits to Everest from the Nepalese government today.

September 30

Tomorrow we fly into Lukla and begin. Toby is so excited he probably won't need the plane. I keep going over our supplies and he keeps reading snatches of the New Testament to me in Greek, without translation, and then practically shouts, "You see, Loren? You see?" This is a strange mission and I keep wondering now, half a world away from home, what the point of it all is. What have I let Toby talk me into? What if the plane crashes? What if I wake up one night with altitude sickness and asphyxiate in my own body fluid? Is what we're doing going to shake a complacent Western Christianity to such an extent that the sleeping giant will awake and turn the world upside down again? It is a little affair between two men and their God and I am less than eager.

October 1

We never made it. Took off and came back after going half-way. Bad weather at Lukla. Met the wife of Doug Scott, one of the two mountaineers to make it to the top of Everest on this expedition. She was going up to meet them. We said we'd like to meet her husband and the others. She said it would be easy. Her and Doug have friends in Canada. She was very disappointed when we had to turn back.

October 2

Today, never even left the airport. Bad weather, clouds, at Lukla (which is almost 10,000 feet).

October 3

We made it!

The plane came in, circled twice, too much cloud, headed back to Kathmandu. Then it turned around again because the clouds broke and came in for a landing at this little airstrip hemmed in by rock, mountains, hills, and on a slope that slants upwards! Bump, bump, lurch, grind, WHAM! Strips's about 200 yards, no more. Broken wings and tailfins and fuselages litter both sides of the runway. Air cool and fresh. Sherpa village, sherpas all around. Somewhat shy. Finally a kid about 15 came and asked if we needed a porter. "Yes," Toby said, "16 rupees a day but you get your own food." "OK." So we got A-tim-bah (that's how his name's pronounced but it's spelt Angtimba). Toby gave him our tent, our three pound can of powdered milk, our canteens, our cold weather jackets. About 15 pounds of gear. The Sherpas all chuckled at the little load he had.

We ate some rice and a soup made of cabbage and potato which was incredibly tasty. Also tea or chiyaa. Cost—seven rupees, which is 70 cents. I let the Sherpas check out my Kukuri (Gurkha knife), they said it wasn't really great but it was okay. I got it in Pokhara. It's got a strong blade though it's seven years old. Much better than the ones you buy on the streets in Nepal which are very cheap and made for tourists.

I gave three children some sweets. A lady in Kathmandu told me they didn't like sweets up in the mountains, it wasn't part of the Sherpas' diet. Was she wrong! The kids dropped everything and cupped both hands shyly towards me as I gave them the candies. They even licked the cellophane the candies were wrapped in.

Half-hour hike to Angtimba's village. At his house we had silver dollar-sized potatoes which had been baked. You peel them and pop them in your mouth. We also had chiyaa. Then Toby and I rearranged our packs and gave Angtimba our two 16 ounce tins of peanut butter and I also gave him my six tins of processed cheese. That got rid of my bulky tinned stuff that was crunching my biscuits.

We're heading out again this afternoon. Those ascents are tough on the heart and legs. We're at a mountain stream and Angtimba just now came down from the house to say, "We go!" Toby had been chipping away at a rock like mica and had attracted some children. Wish I had more candy on me. Even Angtimba's hacking away at the shiny, plastic-like rock. The breeze is cool but the sun is hot. Now we've got seven kids, all with baskets and stuff on their backs, some with rings through their noses. Everybody's watching the tiny bits of mica fly.

evening

Resting, tent set up (to an audience). Toby's Kukuri broke off at the hilt. We were out scrounging wood for a fire. I skinned my shin tripping over rocks. Hard to find dry wood. Got some kindling and a damp tree stump.

Angtimba went like crazy when we left his village of Chaunrikharka. He took three steps for every one of mine and was nimble as a goat. Sherpa dogtrot. But he did stop for rests. We asked him to slow a little bit so we could enjoy the scenery better. Yet after Gumila I left him and Toby and took off down the path with long, quick strides. I passed lots of

Sherpas with their basket loads. Maybe it's because I gave Angtimba the peanut butter to carry. I was marvellously full of energy. Lots of level ground. Looks exactly like the foothills of the British Columbia Rockies, big, green and full of pine trees. White water river too, which we crossed at various points on Edmund Hillary's bridges. On ascents and descents I found it tough. That's when I sweat.

Granola tonight. Milk. Vitour (hot chocolate). Maybe some glucose in the morning. We came ten miles today. Not far from Namche Bazar. Must get there tomorrow because it is Saturday and that is market day and that is supposed to be a sight to behold, a Sherpa bazaar. Maybe Toby can get another Kukuri.

October 4
Namche Bazar

The sun keeps struggling to cut through the grey and white clouds which swirl and immerse the hilltops here. Elevation—12,000 feet. It was rough getting here. We left Benhar after a cool but not cold night. We had our fire at supper time. I had hot milk and granola along with crackers and peanut butter. The granola sure filled me up. It gets very dark in the mountains and once the sun goes, so do the people. If they move about on the path or from house-to-house, they use blazing wood torches which produces a strange effect on me. I feel I am far back in the past. I gave Angtimba a cube of my Swiss fruit tea to try and I guess he liked it. We went to bed about nine. A crazy dog kept me awake by barking most of the night. But I did get some rest. Tea, chiyaa, in the morning, digestive biscuits and Nebisco glucose biscuits and we're on our way.

Hard going. Climb, climb, climb, steep, steep, steep, staircase after staircase of loose rock and stone, curling up from the whitewater rapids to the tops of the foothills. Toby had a hard time, fell far behind. My trick was to take steps one-third of the size I normally take and also to slacken my pace considerably. It was the only way. My heart would have exploded in that thin air.

When the sun is covered it is very cool. Perhaps we will need our Gore-tex jackets tonight. Last night the clouds dissipated for awhile and the stars came out in huge crystal clusters, flickering and flashing like drops of water in the sunlight. But the beautiful thing was this huge white mountain which seemed suspended in the darkness of the night, pure and white and shimmering. I believe it is called Thamserku but it seemed like Shangri-la. The only appropriate song to sing was *O Holy Night*. It was a good night for being at peace.

I have to blow on this pen to keep it going. Waiting for my favourite Nepali food, hot cabbage and potato soup and rice. And chiyaa. I'm cold. We had some noodle soup today at one rest stop. Never again. It was full of chilli. My throat and lips burned up. I had to take one spoonful, gulp, and then slug down some tea to save my life. Biscuits continue to be a good filler. I hope they last. I have eight packages.

Toby sat hunched over a notepad after today's trek. No bazaar. Then he gave me the notepad to read. He asked me what I thought of it. Fine, I told him.

I think we are given situations by God that quite deliberately are not answerable to logic or sound theology or philosophy or even Biblical knowledge but simply to relationship with God and even then, God may be silent. At such times, we can only act in courage and in faith in that silence. There are no rules to appeal to, no guidelines. There is no formula. Only the heart and the soul. And the God we knew before the silence. This was Abraham's plight with the sacrifice of his son Isaac. What our own desperate decisions mean, what they mean to God and to eternity, we have no immediate way of knowing. We cannot tell if they are right or wrong. At these times, we are in a realm of God's grace we cannot fathom. Here truly we walk by faith and not by sight or certainty, except in that certainty that God is love and knows our hearts and our truest desires and intentions. He knows why Dietrich Bonhoeffer laid down his pacifism to take up the sword against Adolph Hitler. We can argue about the rightness or wrongness of it. But Bonhoeffer walked in a different realm than we, far beyond our sound thinking and our precise theological formulations. And, in the end of all ends, he walked with God.

October 6

The beauty is too much to take. What can I use to describe it? Yesterday we had the most overflowing day of trekking yet after leaving Namche Bazar. Level path so no pain. Lots of waterfalls. Big slopes smothered in fir trees. In what we called Rainbow Valley—because the sun formed a rainbow on twirling water vapour below us—we sat in cool, fresh air and clouds kept swirling in and spinning all around us, breaking apart, turning somersaults, we were actually sitting among the clouds at 12,000 feet. The sky is a very rich blue. When the peaks come through they are incredibly white and pure. When we came down into the valley yesterday (Sunday) the trees were deciduous and orange and yellow leaves were strewn everywhere. White streams gurgled through the groves. The smell was of moist autumn in sunshine. Canada. Very surprised to smell and feel this 12,000 miles away.

We had been feeling dizzy in Namche on Sunday morning (but trekking we felt fantastic). Saturday night we shared peanut butter, hot chocolate and some Swiss fruit tea with Angtimba and the woman whose house we camped nearby. They loved the peanut butter. We ate her rice (very hot, lots of chilli) and bought some chocolate bars she had received from members of past and present British mountaineering expeditions (Cadbury's). You certainly crave a lot of sweets with this kind of hiking.

Today promises to be tough. We are headed for Thyangboche, the last big place (it even has an airstrip nearby). Yesterday we met Sherpas walking home from the Everest Expedition (some had t-shirts saying BRITISH EVEREST EXPEDITION). Talked to one who had been at Camp Three, 24,000 feet. He said the British would be flying out of Thyangboche today. I don't think we'll catch them. The trek is mostly ascent today, so it will be little steps, slow, resting frequently.

Last night we camped by a glacier stream so cold your spoons and forks stick to your skin when you try to clean them in the water. Toby changed his mind about taking a bath. I teased him about the necessity of Warrior Christianity but he did not laugh. We had a fire and I had granola and hot chocolate and cheese. Filled to bursting. My Gore-tex jacket is extremely useful. It insulates my sleeping bag from the ground so that I stay warm as toast at night.

"Soon we go," says Angtimba now.

evening
Thyangboche

I seem to have acquired a tremendous sweet tooth up here. I cannot exaggerate the importance of a sour fruit-flavoured candy to suck on, how it improves the saliva flow and makes your mouth happy as you labour up the narrow mountain paths.

Last night was a place called, I think, Puchkin, where the glacier stream was. It was not on our Royal Geographic Society map. Puchkin was full of prayer wheels run by water. Prayers are written on pieces of paper which are glued to drums that have paddles which are placed in the water. Everytime the drum spins over another prayer is sent soaring upwards to heaven.

Now, as I write, Everest itself is obscured by cloud ahead of me, while all around me cow bells are ringing, and yak bells too, in this huge pasture rimmed with houses and a Buddhist monastery. It was a hard climb and the sun was hot, but as we entered Thyangboche a gong started sounding from the monastery. We talked with a few of the bald monks, several of them very young, 18, 19 or 20, and they played about with my pocket camera, trying to look through all its holes at Everest. I gave them some candy. Every Sherpa likes candy. Even Angtimba.

This is our fourth day out. Only sign of altitude sickness was our dizziness at Namche. We are supposed to be alert for the darkening of our urine, chronic blurred vision, and insomnia. The story on the trail that unnerves me a bit is the one about the Japanese girl last spring. Extremely fit, she practically ran from Lukla to Base Camp in two days. She came awake in the night choking on her own body fluids that were bursting through her. She died. I have a medication called Lasix Frusemide which releases excess body fluid but I guess she didn't have any. Swashbuckling Horatio Toby is content to take it slowly and so am I.

When we stop in the evening Toby withdraws and keeps on writing. I doubt I see all of it but he just handed me his notebook again, which he calls *Ruminations*.

We are in need of an honest Christianity, one that will acknowledge everything, the light, the dark, the murky, one that will acknowledge the reality of all the vagaries of human existence and Christian experience. We are in need of a Christianity that will express the vicissitudes of life in all its preaching and teaching and in its art and discipleship, one that will speak not only of joy but of suffering, not only of answered prayer but unanswered prayer, not only of faith but of the loss of faith. Yet one that will paint and write not only of despair but of hope, not only of tragedy but of miracle, not only of mystery but of revelation. It is not as if Christianity has no example of this. Blinded and bewitched by our own ill-conceived but well-intentioned deception and hagiography, we no longer see the Word of God itself, with its full play of light and shadow, of happiness and pain, of victory and disaster. Nor do we plainly see any longer the Word of God himself, with all his fullness of joy and suffering, of answered prayers and his unanswered prayer at Gethsemane, of his mother who believed, and then who did not believe, and then who believed again, of his anger and his frustration at his apostles, and his sarcasm and scorn for the Pharisees, and his fury at the materialism and greed of the Temple, of his broken heart at a friend's grave. How easy it should be to present God's true face to the earth that needs to see it, if only we ourselves saw it again in the Word and lived that Word to such an extent God's honest face became the Church's own face, not in doctrine only, but in reality. Instead, we try to exhibit a Christianity without flaws, a Temple without dark corners, and a God who could never have imagined the Book of Job or the Book of Ecclesiastes or the failures of the children of Israel, let alone put them in the Word of God itself. We sell a God that never knew the cold dark of Gethsemane.

October 7
Periche

Now we are 20 kilometres from Everest.

We came ten kilometres today but you'd think it had been twice that. There wasn't much steep ascent—it was gradual. But suddenly our elevation is 14,000 feet. Wasn't so easy to pray and think to myself today. Just sucked candies and counted 1-2-3-4. The place today is Periche and this has to be a westward sweep of the Mongolian steppes. Vaste wasteland of scrub and glacier rubble and boulders. Canadian Shield. Cold wind flowing. When the sun goes down we may freeze. Can't find a good place to pitch the tent.

Last night we had potato and cabbage soup, my favourite, and rice. Lots of lemon tea. The Buddhist monks made the food. Quite cheap for this expensive part of the country. Toby and I each had a huge plate of rice, a bowl of our favourite soup, and some tsang (pronounced chung, it's the Sherpa beer). Tsang looks like milk. It's made from rice and is very potent and sour. We preferred our glasses of chiyaa. Only 13 rupees. Angtimba took us to see the old lama at the monastery and we came bearing gifts. Toby gave him a box of matches, a roll of candy, and one of his ruminations carefully printed out. I gave him some gum and a small Bible which

Angtimba told him was a holy book. He gave us several prints he'd made on rice paper from his own wood cuts. One huge one of three Buddhas he gave to Toby, me he gave two prayer prints. I also bought one of the wood blocks carved with a design that he used to make some of his prints.

This close to Sagarmatha (Nepalese for the Big Boy) you run into trekkers coming back. While the main body of trekkers is still to come behind us, you meet a few who have made it and a lot who haven't. Just today a woman and a man who never made it—altitude sickness. Some Americans we met last night saw Chris Bonnington and the expedition team but the Brits were quite sickly and not inclined to talk. The weather had turned sour at Base Camp so the expedition broke early. Plus, they lost one of their team on Everest. We missed Bonnington at Thyangboche by two nights. The night he and the team slept at Thyang we camped at Namche Bazar.

This morning I got up early to watch sunrise on Everest. Very brilliant and fresh. Light was tricky (as always). Hope my camera comes through. Thyangboche is surrounded by beautiful snow-streaked peaks which are usually only visible in the early morning before the clouds descend. From Periche it is the Khumbu Glacier of Everest.

October 9
Lobuche

A snowfall at 16,000 feet.

My sleep at Periche was very poor. We had to sleep indoors because there was no suitable ground for the tent. Listening to the mice scampering through the dirt walls I tried to fall asleep, but then the Sherpa women got together and began to sing and dance. It lasted several hours. The Sherpa porters sang and beat on pots and drums. The women linked arms in a line and shuffled back and forth as they wailed, raising dust from the dirt floor. I felt like I was in a Sioux or Blackfoot village. It was wonderful and exasperating at the same time, since I was desperate for sleep. After the dancing stopped they brought a German fellow in to sleep next to me. He was drunk and reeked of tsang, awful smell. Then I couldn't find a good position to sleep in. I tossed and turned and slept in half-hour intervals. In the morning Toby informed me that he had had his most refreshing sleep on the whole trek.

We left Periche's stone huts early yesterday morning and headed for

Lobuche, the last outpost of civilization. It was not easy. There was not just one steep ascent like on our approach to Namche, which eventually came to an end. We kept going sharply up and up. Thousands of years ago the Khumbu Glacier covered this land. Now it is bleak and full of huge boulders and stone. How it crept and crept upwards, sapping our strength. I picked up a headache (which is still with me). How long it was and painfully slow, the higher the altitude, the harder it is to exert yourself, the harder it is to breathe. We finally got to Lobuche, two or three stone huts. We dumped our gear in an old man's hut and set up our tent overlooking a glacial stream. Had fried potatoes and fried noodles and chocolate bars. Then as it got dim we dived into our sleeping bags, knowing it was going to be frosty. I placed my jacket under my bag to insulate it from the ground. I slept fairly well and dreamed a lot, mostly of my wife and children. Just before dawn I opened the tent flap and looked out. SNOW. At least an inch of white powder over everything. The sky was clear and all the huge white mountain peaks were arrayed around us to north, south, east and west. It was cold. Once the sun popped over the mountain peaks (away east towards Everest and China) it got hot. We took a lot of pictures. The world was glittering in the fresh snow—the peaks were all coated and creamy.

Just now Sherpas are returning from Base Camp, porters for a German group. The Germans are saying there was snow yesterday and today at Base Camp. Tomorrow we make for Kala Pattar, a high point from which you can see Everest better. I hope I can make it, for it is an actual peak and, I think, close to or over 18,000 feet. An American doctor we have gotten to know on this trek made it in just now with his Sherpa guide, but had to leave his wife behind in Periche. She didn't feel it was worth it anymore. An Australian that we've also gotten to know on this trek turned back at Periche because his vision was blurring. Over 50% never make it to Base Camp or Kala Pattar. I think we have decided on Kala Pattar rather than Base Camp because you cannot see Everest from Base Camp and Kala Pattar is a higher point.

Noodles with chilli for lunch to try and break up this headache. The sun comes out now and then. My head throbs. But everyone gets this from the altitude. I'm free of all the severe symptoms—inability to pass urine, nausea, vomiting. I'll go as far as I can go but I don't mean to die up here.

Toby handed me another of his scratchings just now. I guess the altitude agrees with him and his creativity.

Some day soon we Christians will have to make up our minds whether we are in it for the numbers or for the kingdom, for the latter may mean 12 and not 12,000. Some day soon we will have to make up our minds whether it is about free enterprise or the freedom of the children of God, for the former emphasizes competition between denominations and not co-operation, it produces retail outlets that focus on sales and profit and customer service, not the body of Christ that serves without remuneration and which gives away the salvation of God without a price tag attached. Some day soon we will have to decide whether we are professionals or simply a humble rank and file who follow a man who happened to rise from the dead.

Are our pastors to be CEOs or lovers? Are our churches to be known for compassion or competition? It is not a matter of what people will flock to or what the weakest part of ourselves feels most comfortable with. When will ethics and principle and right and wrong matter more to Christianity than whatever trend works to pull people in? North America proclaims its renewal movements and the size of its churches and the overwhelming numbers of its converts, but still the continent languishes and the justice system falters and the morals crumble and the politicians cheat and the children are raped and murdered and sold into prostitution and pornography.

Something does not ring true. Someday soon we Christians will have to make up our minds about the lies we tell and the spells we spin that protect us from having to change or repent of what we like, especially when what we like has been created and established by our own hands. Someday soon honesty will have to matter more to us than appearances and success. Someday soon truth will have to matter more than performance and statistics. Someday soon we will have to stop playing God. Someday soon we will have to give up our big ambitions and simply admit that we are poor and hungry and naked and wretched and blind. So that Christ must come again and meet our needs and save the earth.

"So?" Toby asked me when I had finished reading this most recent of his meditations.

"So. You're angry."

"Am I right?"

"God knows."

"Do I sound right sometimes?"

"Sometimes."

"So?"

"So sometimes Christianity is vibrant and still doesn't change the world. For three hundred years we were vibrant and we still got thrown to the lions, Rome remained wicked and her emperors perverse."

"They didn't claim to be a wholescale renewal movement, did they? They were like a guerrilla movement, they were underground, they lived what they believed was right regardless of their numbers or the possibly fatal consequences. We're a fat cat living in the lap of secular luxury whining that we've changed everything for the better when all we've done is adapted well enough to suit ourselves. You want to compare apples with apples? Compare Whitefield and Wesley and Wilberforce's century with ours. That world changed. Courts were affected. Prostitution was affected. Alcoholism was affected. The slave trade was ended and almost a million slaves were set free. Politics was turned upside down. England was turned inside out. There is no comparison."

"So there's no God in North America, right, Toby? He's up here."

"The monks certainly think so."

"We have our monks too, Toby. We have our Trappists and our Franciscans and our Eastern Orthodox hermits that are just as wild and wonderful and eccentric as these Buddhists."

"Sure. Evangelicals are really big on monasticism, aren't they?"

"I thought we were talking about all of Christianity. You think there aren't any non-monastic Buddhist movements?"

"Maybe that's what we need. An evangelical monastic movement to join with the other Christian monastics and provide a little antivenin for all the busy, busy, busy, brag, brag, brag of the rest of evangelicalism."

"You're breathing rarefied air, Toby."

"I can take it into the valley."

"No, you can't."

"Then maybe I need to stay awhile. Up here with the Big Boy."

"The winters would kill you. The winds are over 100 miles an hour and the snow and cold would break your bones. Even the Sherpas move down below. Even your monks."

"I'll get close to the Big Boy. He'll take care of me."

"You get that close to the Big Boy and he'll kill you."

"A slow death down below. A swift mercy up here. What's the difference?"

"You're talking crazy at 16,000 feet."

"God's people ought to be a little bit crazy in this world. If we start to sound normal it means we've bought in."

"You think you can win all your battles with your rhetoric and your pithy aphorisms?"

"I'm Nelson, remember? I don't lose. How's your head?"

"Drumming."

"Still going up?"

"I'm going up."

"Don't take any chances."

"I'll board any frigate you board. Even the big ones."

"A wise Christian rocks no boats, Pastor Loren."

"Perhaps I have a touch of the altitude too, Doctor Toby."

Our talk petered away. Once the night arrived the clouds disappeared and revealed Sagarmatha. It was naked to our eyes, stone and cold and ten thousand years of ice, and under the sharp moon and stars it was fierce and did not burn kindly.

October 11
Thyangboche

Spent the night of October 10th in Periche, trekking there from Lobuche in maybe 90 minutes, a far cry from the three hours it took to come up, but most of it was downhill this time around. Bleak old Periche with all its "mountain man" atmosphere, kerosene lanterns, candles, smokey fire, dirt floor, stone walls, and flea-ridden dogs. Fences made of stones placed together without mortar, exactly like Ireland and Scotland. Set up the tent—couldn't last time because of the lumpy ground—because the Korean team which is attempting Everest's summit in two years (next year is the Spanish) was just returning from Base Camp and had filled Periche's two so-called hotels. Found a bamboo mat, placed it over the lumpy ground, put up the house.

My last time at Periche a drunk that reeked to high heaven slept practically on top of me, the women sang and danced all night, I never slept, and I picked up a headache. This night was an encore. You'd think the Koreans had already climbed Everest. They started warming up while I had potatoes (a plate of the small potatoes that you peel with your fingers) and pancakes (pan-size), peanut butter, biscuits, hot chocolate. By the time I hit the sack the Koreans were pushing aside plates of rice and fish and seaweed and popping open bottles of some strong clear-as-water wine (not to mention glasses of tsang). A sing-song started. A man stumbled out into the dark, fell into the tent, and put his foot into my neck. Sometime around one in the morning the voices died and I fell into a fitful sleep. In the morning it was cold, bleak and dreary, the wind slicing across the boulders and flatland scraped down by the receding Khumbu Glacier thousands of years before. Then the sun came out and as I trekked down-hill towards Thyangboche the big mountains appeared behind me. Twenty-four hours before I'd been close enough to those giants to touch them.

There had been a lot of us expecting to make Kala Pattar and they included three Canadians, a German, a Dane, two Americans and an Englishman. The night before K.P. we had potatoes and rice, all crouched around the small fire in the earth floor in the old man's hut with no chimney. My stomach was not up to the occasion and I had only a bit of food. (My bad stomach was not due to the altitude, but to two bowls of boiled noodles I'd had earlier on, placed in some sauce that played havoc with my belly.) We looked at each other in the firelight, ate and drank, hoped none of us would get altitude sickness overnight, and went to bed. Toby and I to our little green tent.

It had snowed the night before. The stars were chips of ice, winking crushed clusters of them, and the mountains loomed up ahead, blue, white and purple in the night sky. I couldn't sleep, couldn't find a good position, couldn't keep my feet from feeling cold. Not a minute of unconsciousness for ten hours. I hummed tunes, thought of stories, prayed, thought about Nicole and the children. Then the curse—urination. Warm in my bag, I refused to climb out and freeze to death. Hours passed of vain conflict. I got dressed, got out of my bag, screamed silently at the stars, froze to death and crawled back into my bag with my clothes still on. An hour or so later: "CANADIAN!" The German woke us up. It was around 5.30 A.M. By noon clouds usually cover the peaks, so it is imperative to reach Kala Pattar by nine or ten if you are to see anything and everything.

Toby and I got up, got dressed, got on our heavy Gore-tex and down jackets. You could see yellow light behind the peaks (you cannot see Everest or most of the peaks from Tobouche, only a few). We left first with the Danish fellow who'd lived in Nepal for seven months—he was a student of anthropological studies—and strided out over the trail, too impatient to wait, afraid of clouds coming in. Our Sherpas and the German stayed for tea and we left them too.

The first part of the trail was a flat green valley. It was still cold, below freezing. But my headache of the previous day was gone and I felt fine. Toby appeared to be struggling. We moved quickly. The Dane dropped behind and the German (whom we knew to be in great shape) caught up with us. The walk got tough. Ascent into moraine. The sun was creeping up the white mountain walls but our valley was still in shadow. Tons and tons of glacial debris. Loose rocks and square boulders as big as houses. Difficult to see the trail. Keep eyes peeled for small cairns of stone placed on boulders as trail markers. Hard to breathe. Through nose and mouth at the same time.

A prehistoric feeling. Only the three of us, picking our way over the ancient Khumbu Glacier, slipping on ice-coated stones over glacial streams, feeling the blue deepen in the sky, watching the sunlight slide down golden along the mountain peaks, hearing lonesome and weird bird calls, almost like a gurgling, something from a primitive swamp at the dawn of time. I felt again my childhood fascination with dinosaurs and indeed, you expected a Tyrannosaurus Rex to rear up its massive head behind a mountain at any moment. Just at the base of Kala Pattar was a vast and empty stretch of flat white sand. Silent across the wasteland we walked, under the shadow of Kala Pattar, Everest just a few kilometres away.

We began a 45 degree ascent up Pattar because we didn't know where the trail was. The slope was lumpy and mossy. Steep. Hard to breathe. Frequent rests. Going up in tight loops. The German takes the lead. The sun finally hits us. Toby and I dump our heavy jackets on a rock. Up. Up. Up. Leave Toby behind. The German attains the North-West Ridge but I approach from the front, the West Face, and am soon clambering over big, firm black boulders. Hands and legs, on all fours, now really mountain climbing. Panting. Can't see Toby. Up, over, up, up. Sweat. Fast breathing. White mountains all around. Hand over hand. Lift, heave, breathe. Up, up, up. Cairn of rocks. Summit? No. Past the cairn. Finger-hold. Lift.

"HO!" I yell and the German jerks his head around. "Hello!" he laughs and I am the second one to the summit.

And all around us the top of the world: Everest (South-West Face), Nuptse, Lhotse, Chomo Lonzo, Nupla, Kang Cho, Thamserku, Kangtega, Baruntse, Makalu, Taboche, Cholatse, Ama Dablam, 29,800 feet, 26,000 feet, 21,000 feet, 25,000 feet, 27,000 feet. The monsters of the mountains.

How wild and strong and good Everest is from the South-West Face. Blue sky. No clouds. Great purity and clearness. The feeling! The air was cool and fresh, the sun was high and its light warmed the stark granite and seemed to soften its sharp face, wisps of white drifted over the peak. On October 10th only three climbers attained the summit of Kala Pattar—one German and two Canadians, myself and another fellow from Alberta. But not Toby.

He stopped a hundred feet or so from the summit. The Dane likewise. The Englishman quit on the trek to Kala Pattar. The Americans got to the base of Kala Pattar and turned back. My body had been tough enough to make it. How good it felt to be unique. But I wasn't so much proud and exhilarated as at peace with the knowledge I could go further. And we did, climbing (painfully) to Upper Kala Pattar (from 18,100 feet to 18,500 feet) to get a view of Everest's South Call. We were able to see Base Camp, the Ice Fall, the whole approach to Everest's summit. Then the other two clambered up another few hundred feet to 18,800, but it was enough for me to stay at 18,500. I could do no more. I was close enough and high enough and the Big Boy overwhelmed me in a massive silence. Tomorrow morning, here at Thyangboche, Everest will emerge and flicker white and hard in the dawn, then come softly as the sun rises to the full. I will see him one more time.

It is very nice to have done this, to have accomplished it. Soon, I hope, I will have learned the lesson well and never give up on anything of consequence.

I hoped Toby would forgive me for remaining on the summit so long. I knew I would never be there again. I found him sitting on the rock where we'd tossed our jackets.

"Are you all right?" I asked him.

"Well done, Hardy," he responded, naming Nelson's right hand man. "I need your help now."

"What's wrong?"

"I can't urinate and my vision is so bad I'm almost blind. Help me down."

I put my arm around him and we began the descent as quickly as he could manage. Thank God that the altitude dropped swiftly. He recovered rapidly at Periche, despite the singing Koreans, and now he is almost his old self here at Thyangboche. He is moving his pen slowly across his notepad.

Just now he looked up. "Did you leave anything up there?" he asked me.

"Yes."

"What?"

"I scratched my name on the underside of a rock."

"What else?"

"I left a note. A few lines from a poem really."

"Tell me the lines."

"Cold he may seem, and divine, for many have sought his face and died. But when the sun is higher than he, I have seen warm black arms reach out to gather his children in. I have felt broad arms lift us nearer to heaven and no mortal dead breathes the air we breathe."

He was scratching away at his pad. "And who wrote that?"

"I did, Toby," I told him. "It was just a passing thought."

He smiled, his black growth of beard making him appear as swarthy as a buccaneer. He only needed one of the Sherpa boys' gold rings. "Perhaps the altitude is as good for you as it is for me, Pastor Loren."

"There is nothing like a breath of fresh air, Doctor Toby."

"So I understand."

October 16
morning

We came down fast. Thyangboche was full of tents and French tourists. All the way back down we ran into trekkers or tourists, differentiated by who carries the weight. The rich tourists never carry any pack and they hardly ever go past Thyangboche. We discovered the Royal Nepalese Airlines were bringing in FIVE airloads a day into Lukla (not to mention Thyanboche which, as I've mentioned earlier, has its own airstrip). When we had gone up, all we saw were Sherpas. Now all we saw were Europeans and Japanese. We were very glad we'd been among the first ten up to Thyangboche.

We had promised Angtimba a Coke so we laboured up a steep slope a few hours out of Thyang to reach the Everest View Hotel ($60 a single per night, $157 for a double, meals included). Here we were able to cash some traveller's cheques as our money was very low. We had our Cokes (one dollar apiece) and steak sandwiches, read some old issues of *TIME, NEWSEEK,* and *NATIONAL GEOGRAPHIC.* Angtimba looked happy but ill-at-ease in the high class surroundings. I think he would have been happier to eat with his fingers. E.V. Hotel has a long way to go in terms of interior decoration. Only primer seemed to be on the walls and it was icy. Still, it was a bit of fun to be there among the super-rich who fly into Thyangboche at 13,000 feet and then take a thirty minute stroll from landing strip to hotel. One lady near us actually said "N'yes" several times during a chat with another circle-glassed woman, one man already had altitude sickness (or maybe two), one woman said she never left the hotel at night because it was too cold, and one young fellow wanted to go trekking but worried aloud that the walk from the hotel to Thyangboche (mostly downhill) might be too difficult. We left in a hurry.

Passed huge yaks on a short jaunt past Khumjung (where Edmund Hillary has built a school and hospital), down a steep descent (jolt-jolt-jolt) to Namche Bazar where we pitched our tent in the same place we had eight or nine days before. A stone house they had just begun to break rock for with a sledge hammer when we'd come through earlier now had its grey stone walls one-third of the way up. Incredibly fast. The new look in solid thick-walled stone houses is impressive (all the stones are fitted closely together, I'm not sure with mortar or not) and they only cost $2000 or 20,000 rupees. No central heating or plumbing, of course.

In Namche I felt ill. To go all the way to 18,500 feet and feel fine, then trot down to 10,000 feet and feel bad. It turned out it was constipation. To ensure I was never debilitated by dysentery on our last few days up to Kala Pattar I had taken MexaForm. It had worked and now I was shut down tight. After some hot chilli and noodles and numerous excursions to the bushes my cramps and nausea left me.

On Monday, October 13th, we moved down from Namche to Lukla. We stopped a lot. There were kids to tease, a few Canadian trekkers, a big American mountaineering group, an important lama draped in red and orange robes hobbling along with the help of an aluminum ski pole, his porter walking slowly ahead. We reached Angtimba's house late that afternoon and this time his father was home, a pleasant and fit-looking man with Caucasian features but also a strict father, we guessed. Corn was piled in the centre of the floor. There were two floors to the house, the bottom floor being a stable, the second floor a combined bedroom, living room and kitchen. One or two of the women were cornhusking while three men, including or excluding Angtimba's father (not sure in the dim, smokey light) chanted sing-song from three great tabloid-sized holy books. We ate a great plate of freshly boiled corn cobs, gave Angtimba's father a gift of all the boxes of matches we had left (six or seven or more) and jogged off for Lukla, 30 or 40 minutes away.

At last! The real cabbage and potato soup, the stuff I'd been hunting for ever since that day on October 3rd I'd had it for the first time. But nowhere on the trek had it been as good as this. Toby had two bowls, I had two bowls, the German and Canadian who'd been on Kala Pattar's summit team with me were there and also had two bowls each. After our meal and a last night's sleep on the mountain it only remained to fly out.

The next morning the plane speared through low white clouds and roared up the landing strip on the slope, closely followed by a second aircraft. Out came the tourists and the trekkers, the sunglasses and the backpacks, the luggage and the camping gear. (Some French tourists brought out a huge wooden picnic table complete with stools, carried by Sherpas, of course.) We got Angtimba lined up with another job. He had the fur cap I'd bought him on his head. It was quick. In a moment I saw him trotting off down the trail, large Himalayan basket on his back loaded with goods. "Nomastay." Have a nice day.

It was hot back in Kathmandu. The following day, October 15th, as planned, Toby and I met up with the American doctor and his wife (Bruce and Elaine), Duane (the other Canadian who made it), and the German at the only French restaurant in Nepal, Chez Armand. Clean, well-cooked food. Onion soup. Chicken fried in butter. French fries, cucumber salad, fresh lemon juice, fresh lime. Cokes. Pineapple rings. Icy cherries. Much talk. The American couple are back to the States after a month or so travelling in India. Duane is seeking entry into New Zealand. The German (Deutchesland we called him) is back for studies by November 1st (sociology major). Toby and I are on to New Delhi and thence quickly home to Canada.

From Chez Armand (with the Nepalese youth who salutes you at the gate) to Pie Street, near Freak Street and New Road (with the Temple of the Living Goddess, who remains such until she menstruates for the first time or unfortunately sheds blood in some other way). We have a round of pie eating. Each of us have from five to seven slices as we go from shop to shop (Chi and Pie, New Style Pie Shop, etc.), including myself with two slices of lemon meringue, a mixed fruit, a dried fruit, a thick slab of banana and chocolate. Toby had at least a whole pie's worth. Plus Cokes. We leave each other in the middle of mouthfuls and go our separate ways. Toby buys a bunch of Nepalese coins dated 2029, Chinese calendar. This year is 2031, the Year of the Monkey. I put mosquito cream on before I fall asleep at the hostel and the big girls buzz, snarl, hop about, then leave me alone for the rest of the night.

night

Leaving tomorrow morning, Friday the 17th.

I'm scrubbed and washed and squeaky clean, all my gear packed and repacked for the bus trip to India. Toby was writing as usual and I asked him when he was going to do his packing. He looked up and shook his head.

"Hardy, old chap, I'm staying here in line of battle."

"What are you talking about now?" I asked him.

"How did you feel your last night at Namche?"

"Namche. I don't know. It was our last night close to the big mountains."

"Can you leave them so easily?"

"I didn't say it was easy. It's like touching the beginning of the world."

"So stay on with me."

"What?"

"Do you really want to see the Big Boy just once in your life?"

"Toby, my life goes on. Everest is wonderful. But it's a mountain."

"Really?"

"Do you still need oxygen? You have a wife and kids. You have a job."

"I wired Cheryl when I went to buy the coins. They'll join me here. I wired the school too. I'm expendable, Loren. They'll hire another wage slave to help them churn out their ministers like pancakes."

"Where are you going to live?"

"Don't worry. We'll winter here. I've already checked into doing some ESL. We'll be quite comfortable. There is a lot of thinking and writing I need to do. Far away from the North American Christian clamour."

"What are you going to do? Shave your head and become a Buddhist?"

"Is that what you're afraid of? I'm sure that just as God brings magi to his Son he also brings Buddhist monks in due season. But no, have no fear, pastor. I'm not abandoning the faith once delivered to the saints. I just need to look past the smoke and mirrors and get to the heart of it. The Nepalese will help me. The Sherpas. The Himalayas. And Sagarmatha."

"Sagarmatha. For the love of God, Toby, that mountain will kill you."

"For the love of God."

"What am I supposed to do? Go back alone?"

"Do whatever you want. Whatever God wants."

"You think I'm one of them? A cheesey pastor who started coasting after his first few church fights? A man of God who's looking for the latest trend to latch onto so that he can fill up his church and write a book about it?"

"No. I don't. You're one of the people who remind me that God is still here, close enough to touch. You probably don't need to be in Nepal, Loren. I do. You have passion and integrity. Go back to where people need it the most."

"You think they don't need Christ in Kathmandu?"

"We need Christ everywhere. But the Nepalese are probably more innocent in rejecting someone they have never known than we Christians in North America are in rejecting someone we knew and found too honest a God for comfort. Go home, Loren. Nazareth needs you more than Nineveh. Here."

He tore a page out of his notebook and gave it to me. "Save it for the first Indian train," he said. "You won't be able to sleep on board those things anyway. Might as well have some reading material."

He went and sat down. "You'd better rest. When does the bus go?"

"Six."

"It's a long trip to Delhi."

So I lay on the cot. Toby turned out the light after another five minutes of scribbling. I guess we both slept. But sometime in the middle of the night I got up to use the toilet down the hall and I took his piece of paper with me.

We are trying to put the best face on Christianity. That is the influence of sales, of retail, of a free enterprise culture: Glamorize your God product if you want people to walk through the doors of your church. It is also the influence of the so-called spiritual warfare model because we always must say and think the best of "our side" if we're in a fight or a contest or a competition. So propaganda enters the picture with legitimacy. The trouble with all of this is that it promotes, even exalts dishonesty as a spiritual good. But the Christianity of the scriptures and of Christ is honest and transparent and reflects struggle and suffering and failure and imper-

fection as well as triumph and joy and attainment and wholeness. Dishonesty can never be justified, no matter what ends it is meant to achieve. Yet contemporary Christianity is less than honest about the pain and failures of the Christian life, as if the admission of such shortcomings might somehow disgrace God. The irony is that it is not our attempt to appear perfect in our lives and churches that honours God but just the opposite. Our confession of our imperfections brings a God of grace and forgiveness into the picture. Yes, people will attend the apparently perfect church. But then they will attempt to live their Christianity by aping that same graceless picture-perfect perfection. They won't succeed. They will blight their souls and the earth. They will wind up either rejecting Christ in the bitterness of their new slavery or they will have to play the immaculate saint and go about masked. They will bring yet more tyranny and pretence upon a world already heavy with tyrants and bewitched by illusion. On the other hand, those few who come to the church where imperfection is acknowledged and confessed will be lifted up by God alone, not by their own pretence or performance, and the wings they grow to soar with will not be waxen and of their own making, but the wings of God, wings like eagles. Humility results in God's presence and brings a great blessing and an honest-to-God Christianity to the earth, something we have far too little of in this generation. Perhaps this is why we no longer paint great pictures or build great architecture or write great literature. Perhaps this is why we cannot produce art of depth and significance to stagger a world of delusion and deceit. Because just like that world, we lie.

I dedicate this thought to my brother Loren. He has been to the mountaintop with his God. It is from there he will find the winds that carry eagles over our earth.

October 17
Enroute to New Delhi

I left well before dawn when Toby was deep in a sleep of flapping sails and charging seas and warriors bright with the armour of God. I put a note by his pillow. It is just one line: *Your name is under the stone.* He will find the note in the morning when the sun rises over Everest and fills all of Kathmandu. And one day when he has climbed Kala Pattar and the sun has risen again he will, perhaps, be able to find that other note, etched on stone. He will need that human touch. For Sagarmatha will be towering over him in all his eternity and magnificence and will blind him to everything else.

CHAPTER *13*

GOOD NIGHT, JOHN KING

It all happened much as I am writing it here. I say this not simply for others who will not find these few months of my life credible but I say it for myself because it was a long time ago and sometimes the edges blur and you lose the shape of the thing you value most. I was there and all of them were there with me. I had to die. But now it is all before me and there is no uncertainty.

My Dad was a teacher but he used to preach in a church on Sundays too. He did that for about ten years. He had studied theology as well as going to teacher's college. Which is why he had a lot of friends in the States who were ministers. That's where he'd gone for his theological training, to Boston University's School of Theology. He'd finished his degree there a year before I was born. I suppose the best friend he made at Boston University was a man he always referred to as M.L. I called him Uncle M.L. because as a young boy I thought he was an uncle who lived in America like Uncle Bill who had moved his family to Chicago. When I was 12 I finally understood that M.L. was Martin Luther King.

"He christened you," Dad would mention to me every birthday. "We went down to his church in Montgomery. You were born the same day the U.S. Supreme Court outlawed segregation in public schools."

"I know, Dad."

"You know what M.L. said? This boy will do great things. He will do things for all the races. He will help to bring all the nations of the earth together. That's what he prayed over you."

"I know, Dad."

I knew. It made me feel an awkward kind of pride, as if I was a peasant that everyone expected to be a prince, but I felt embarrassed by this sort of talk too. I hated it when Dad indulged in his fantasies about me before friends and relatives. My brothers really got sick of it: "I guess Dad should have named you Brown versus Board of Education." But I carried Uncle M.L.'s name and Dad's name, John King Peterson.

I say all this to explain why Dad was always heading down to the States in the '60's from our home in Canada. He was joining Uncle M.L.'s marches. I'm surprised they let him over the border. He kept telling the U.S. customs officials he was going down for religious conventions. If he'd ever been arrested at one of the marches they probably would have denied him access. He did get his head cracked a few times and worried my mother to death but he never got thrown behind bars.

Anyway, in 1968 Dad decided the whole family ought to join him. He assured Mom it was going to be a peaceful march. "The worst battles have all been fought," he convinced her. So we piled into the green station wagon with the strips of wood down each side, three brothers and one sister and Dad and Mom up front, and we did a long drive down to Tennessee, the kind that fills your car with hamburger wrappers and empty Coke bottles and balled up napkins. We did the trip in March when Canada was still cold and blustery. My brothers and sister and I thought we'd soon be eating popsicles and ice cream and wearing cut-offs. We hit Memphis on March 19th and three days later a blizzard dumped 16 inches of snow on the city.

"This is ridiculous," my older brother Andy complained. "Even Canada doesn't have this much snow left."

The march was postponed. Dad met with Uncle M.L. briefly before he had to fly to New York. I heard Dad say something to Mom in the motel room when he thought we were all asleep. "M.L.'s depressed," he whispered. I felt scared lying there in my bed, Andy snoring next to me. Uncle M.L. was larger than life. Men like that weren't supposed to have problems. I wasn't even sure what depression was but I knew that when Mom said she was depressed she looked sad and grim and smoked too many cigarettes and wanted to sleep all day.

The march went off as planned on a Thursday, March 28th, but it was a disaster. Some teens and some young men started breaking windows and fighting with the police. Uncle M.L. shouted that he would not lead a violent march so he called it off. We took a taxi back to the motel and I didn't see anything except a lot of police cars. But over 100 stores were damaged by the rioting and a boy only a bit older than me was shot dead by the police. The governor of Tennessee sent thousands of National

Guardsmen into Memphis. Mom was terrified, Dad was angry at the violence, my brothers and I were excited at seeing all the soldiers with real guns. We stayed huddled in our motel room which didn't make Mom feel any better. It was the Lorraine and it was an African American motel. But no one bothered us. A number of people who'd taken rooms in the motel were friends and supporters of Uncle M.L.

I had never seen Uncle M.L. before the march on Thursday. He was supposed to stay at the Lorraine but he couldn't make his way through the rioting to get to it. On Friday he flew to Atlanta and Dad phoned him a couple of times. One call they did a lot of laughing so we all felt better cooped up there in the motel room. No riot would ever break out again and all the world would turn out right.

The next Wednesday, April 3rd, I was walking around the parking lot watching the sky because the TV had said tornado warnings were out for Memphis. I wanted to see a long black Wizard of Oz snake twist and twirl down. That's when a bunch of cars pulled up and Uncle M.L. got out of one of them. He saw me and grinned.

"I recognize you. You're John's boy, aren't you? You're John King."

"Yes, sir."

"This is about your birthday, isn't it, John King?"

"Another month, Uncle M.L., in May."

"Ralph," he asked one of his friends, "how many years since Brown versus Board of Education?"

It was Ralph Abernathy. He shrugged. "I don't know. It was '54. Got to be 14 years now."

"You're getting old on us, John King," Uncle M.L. laughed, "and we're getting old with you. You think you can get your Daddy to bring you on down to Atlanta for your birthday? Aunt Coretta would throw a fine party for you and Brown. I know Yoki and Marty and Dexter would be happy to meet you."

"I'll ask him, Uncle M.L., as soon as I see him."

"What room are you in?"

"106."

"I'll be right above you in 306. Tell your Dad and Mom I'd love to have them drop by this afternoon."

But Dad and Mom had heard his voice and came out of our motel room. The three of them hugged. Then they all went up to the balcony at 306 while some of Uncle M.L.'s friends went around the front to register and get the key to open the room. I kept watching for the tornado. It didn't start looking like a storm until later in the day when Dad and Mom took us four kids out to eat. Then there was thunder and black clouds and all of a sudden a pouring rain. We went to the church, Mason Temple, about 7.30 and the place was already packed. Uncle M.L. was supposed to speak but he wasn't there.

"M.L.'s exhausted," Mom told us. "They should leave him alone and let him sleep."

But Ralph Abernathy called him. Uncle M.L. was in his pyjamas and just reading and trying to relax. He didn't want to come out. When Dad spoke to Mom about that I understood. I liked being cozy in my room when the big thunderstorms hit back home. But I'd never heard Uncle M.L. make a speech before either and part of me wished he would change his mind and come to the Temple. I even prayed about it. If God wanted Uncle M.L. to rest then he should go to bed. But if God needed Uncle M.L. here to help these people, to help me, God should give him fresh energy.

Uncle M.L. came. The thunder was booming when he got up to the pulpit. There must of been over 2000 people clapping and cheering. He started to talk. At first he seemed so quiet and awkward but then a new strength, like the strength of the storm, burst right out of him. That was the night he quoted Carlyle, that only when it's dark enough you can see the stars, and I remembered that quotation and his speech the rest of my life.

God had let him live now, not when Moses led his people to freedom, and he was happy it had worked out that way. He was happy God had brought him to Memphis right now. He was happy he hadn't died when he'd been stabbed in New York. He was happy he hadn't missed the sit-ins and the marches and the Freedom Rides. He was happy he hadn't missed Albany or Birmingham or Selma. The people began to shout to encourage him to keep talking: "Yes, Doctor! Go ahead, go ahead! Oh, yes! Yes, sir, go ahead!"

"It really doesn't matter what happens now," he said in his strong voice. "I don't know what will happen now. We've got some difficult days ahead. But it really doesn't matter with me now. Because I've been to the mountaintop. Like anybody else I would like to live a long life. Longevity has its place. But I'm not concerned about that now. I just want to do God's will. And he's allowed me to go up to the mountain. And I've looked over and I've seen the Promised Land. I may not get there with you. But I want you to know tonight that we as a people will get to the Promised Land. So I'm happy tonight. I'm not worried about anything. I'm not fearing any man. Mine eyes have seen the glory of the coming of the Lord!"

It was the only time I had ever heard Uncle M.L. and I'd never heard people shout in church like that before. Dad was grinning and clapping: "I could use a congregation like that in Canada." I felt like I was on fire. When we got back to the motel and everybody went to bed, I couldn't sleep. I slipped outside at midnight and walked in circles around the court-yard parking lot, talking to God.

I had believed in God my whole life but it had only been the past December I'd stood up in church and said I believed in Jesus. That decision had been made in the dark of my bedroom where I tossed and turned and couldn't sleep and couldn't make up my mind about how far I was supposed to go with God. Now it was four months later, I couldn't sleep again, and I was asking God again how far I was supposed to go with him.

"What are you doing, John King?"

I looked up. It was Uncle M.L. leaning against the railing of his balcony and smiling down at me.

"Hello, Uncle M.L.," I answered, surprised and embarrassed.

"You seem mighty agitated."

"I'm sorry, sir. I was, well, praying, sort of praying."

"It's late."

"I like praying at night."

"Well. I guess I do too. I guess I'm doing that too."

"I saw you tonight."

"Were you and your family at the Temple?"

"Yes, sir. I really liked it. I liked all the people shouting to encourage you. I liked you."

"I like you too, John King. I hope you get a church like that someday."

A car pulled into the parking lot. A man got out and waved at Uncle M.L. who waved back.

"Come on up, A.D.," Uncle M.L. greeted the man. "This is my brother, John King. He's come in from Louisville. If you're going to keep praying, you pray for our march. They don't want to let us march now because of that riot. But we need to march. We need to help the people here."

"I'll pray, Uncle M.L."

"All right. I'll see you in the morning. Do you like catfish?"

"I've never had it."

"It's delicious. I have to get you to try it this weekend. We'll share one together."

"Okay."

"Good night, Brown versus Board of Education."

I sat out there a long time. I saw some stars coming through the clouds. The light was still on in Uncle M.L.'s room when I went to bed. It was 3.30, the 4th of April, and I felt like I was flying inside. I soared into sleep.

The next day Dad came down from 306 and told us the courts had said we could march on Monday. Mom wanted to get back to Canada so she was glad it would be over in a few days. "We've been down here almost three weeks," she complained.

"It's been all right, hasn't it?" asked Dad.

"The last march wasn't all right."

"No, no. They've taken care of all that. Rap Brown's kids won't do anything this time. They met with them today."

I hung around the parking lot that afternoon, thinking about the catfish. Uncle M.L. spotted me close to suppertime.

"I had catfish for lunch," he told me from his balcony. "I should have called you up. Now I have to go out to Reverend Kyles' tonight. But tomorrow would be a good time for another catfish meal. I promise there won't be a lot of broccoli or asparagus. I'm not interested in broccoli and asparagus much. Are you, John King?"

"I just want to taste the catfish, Uncle M.L."

"Me, too. Will you be at the meeting tonight?"

"Yes, sir. I'm looking forward to it."

"Well, you do some shouting yourself tonight, all right?"

"Yes, Uncle M.L."

"I have to go in and shave. Supper tomorrow. Come up to my room."

"Yes, sir."

"Good night, John King."

"You too, Uncle M.L."

It was cool and I went into the motel room. We were so crowded in there I hated to stay long. The TV was blasting and after awhile Mom couldn't take the noise anymore. She came over and turned it off and Andy and my sister Karen made faces.

"That's enough of that," said Mom. "We're only going to be in

Memphis a few more days. You should get out and look around."

"It's cold out," whined my younger brother Tom.

"Oh, come on," I taunted, "you come from Canada, for pity's sake."

"This comes from Canada!" he yelped and took his pillow and whacked me with it. I grabbed another one right away and belted him back. We began swinging wildly at each other, laughing and shouting.

"Not in here!" Mom came after us. "You'll break something! Go outside!"

A firecracker went off as I opened the door and Andy jumped up from the bed where he'd been sitting with a comic book: "Fireworks!" We stampeded out the door.

"Take cover!" someone yelled in front of us and hid behind our station wagon. It was a bunch of Uncle M.L.'s friends and they were running and throwing themselves down on the cement. Right above my head someone cried out, "Martin's been shot!" Mom came through the door behind us like a streak and looked up at the balcony. Uncle M.L. was sprawled on his back and we could all see the blood. She screamed and threw us four kids back into the room. "Who is it? What is it?" demanded Dad heading for the door from the washroom. But Mom was wild and shoved him back: "Don't go out there, they are shooting out there!" Karen went to the window and Mom yanked her by the arm. "I said they are shooting out there!" she shrieked. "M.L. is hurt! Now stay away from the window and door!" But Dad pushed Mom aside and ran out and up the balcony steps. Mom went after him. And I followed right behind Andy.

I still had the pillow in my hand. I thought I could do something, get Uncle M.L. a glass of water, find some bandages, make him smile. Andy and I went up the balcony after Dad and Mom. Some people were crouched down behind the railing, expecting more shots, but Dad and Mom went right up to Uncle M.L. and Ralph Abernathy and Andrew Young. I was right at Dad's back and I saw Uncle M.L. lying there, his eyes open, and he looked scared. Mom started to cry.

I bent and got down on all fours so I could squeeze past. I thought I ought to put the pillow under Uncle M.L.'s head. But Ralph Abernathy took it from me and tried hard to stop the blood with it. There were sirens and police cars and suddenly two paramedics from an ambulance came and pushed me away. They put Uncle M.L. on their stretcher and carried him down from the balcony. Mom saw me. She took my hand very gently in hers and walked me down to 106 where she asked me to kneel and pray with her. I pushed my face into the bedspread. My throat tightened so much I could not swallow and my nose filled and the tears were sparks on my cheeks.

Dad drove the station wagon to the hospital filled with Uncle M.L.'s friends. We turned the TV back on and soon it was filled with the voices and faces of anchormen talking about Uncle M.L. being shot. He was expected to recover. I never got off the floor, I sat there and let myself cry and looked at the black and white images of Uncle M.L.'s face. Just when I felt inside that my prayers were being answered a man on the TV said Uncle M.L. was dead. He had died at St. Joseph's Hospital a few minutes after seven o'clock. Dad came back an hour later, looking like death, and Mom held him and we were all crying together, even tough Andy, while the TV showed films of Uncle M.L., especially the March on Washington from 1963. When I lay down in the dark to try to sleep I thought about the catfish supper.

There were riots in many cities but in Memphis Aunt Coretta led our march with Marty and Yoki and Dexter on Monday and there was no violence. Our family marched together. I had always thought about marching beside Uncle M.L. but now I just put one foot in front of the other and Dad had his arm around my shoulder.

Bobby Kennedy chartered a private plane to bring Uncle M.L. and his family back to Atlanta. Dad used a credit card and we flew from Memphis to Atlanta that night and found a hotel. Mom never complained about the extra expense. I could hardly breathe the next day the air was so hot and heavy. We stood outside the Ebenezer Church with another 100,000 people. I sat on a curb finally. Mom sat beside me and stroked my hair. Inside the church they began to sing When I Survey The Wondrous Cross and the crowd began to sing it too. I just listened.

I could hear Uncle M.L.'s voice and a part of me said, You see, it's all right, he's alive after all, the TV was mistaken. But it was a game your heart plays. I knew his voice was a recording. I was looking at the hazy blue sky when he said, "I just wanted to leave a committed life behind." Then they brought out the coffin made of African mahogany and placed it in a farm cart. Mom said she'd stay with me and Tom at the church, it was too hot for us to walk, but Tom and I shook our heads and our family headed out again, following the cart and the two mules and the jingling bells of their harness that made me think of snow and pine trees. We stopped at Uncle M.L.'s old college, Morehouse, and the trees were big and cool. I

sat in the green grass and thought about Uncle M.L. being a young student. One of his professors spoke for awhile. I listened to some of it:
"How strange! God called the grandson of a slave on his father's side and
said to him: Martin Luther, speak to America about war and peace. About
social justice and racial discrimination. About its obligation to the poor.
About non-violence as a way of perfecting social change in a world of
brutality and war." The dogwood was blooming at the cemetery and Free
At Last was carved on his stone and I felt like nothing. I wanted to joke
with Uncle M.L. some more but God had said no to that. I did not understand the bright God of my fresh Christian morning anymore, the God
who had come at night in gentleness to live in my soul.

We flew back to Memphis and picked up our station wagon at the airport. I thought we were going to point the car north and head home. I
wanted to go home. There was a river I liked to walk beside and pray. The
Canadian spring would be coming on now too, the oaks and elms and
silver birches opening. I wanted to be alone for a hundred years.

But Dad and Mom had made a decision. Mom never fought it, which
was unlike her. We didn't want to stay in Memphis so we took the I-40 to
Nashville where we rented a room. It had a wobbly round white table and
we sat around it to eat burgers and fries and drink pop.

"Look," Dad said, "we're going to Indiana."

Andy looked at Mom. "What about school?" he asked. "How are we
going to pass?"

"I phoned up, " Dad told us. "What you miss you'll cover in summer
school."

Summer school! I thought I'd been handed a sentence of death.
Petersons always did well in school, so well we received exemptions from
exams and finished in early June. Dad saw our shocked faces.

"Maybe there won't be summer school. We're only going to stay
down here a few more weeks. Your mother and I can't just go back to
Canada as if nothing has happened. It would be like walking out on M.L.
and all the good he tried to do. Just remember that whatever happens
down here affects us up there, okay? So we're going to stay down here
and do something we think M.L. would approve of us doing. We're going
to try and help Bobby Kennedy become the next president of the
United States."

I scarcely knew who Bobby Kennedy was, except that his older brother had been JFK, the American president who had been shot while I was

watching Donald Duck over my school lunchbreak. They had stopped the cartoons to tell us. That day had hurt me because I knew the killing had been a great wrong. None of the mudslinging against the Kennedys I heard in later years ever changed that feeling of pain and violation. It made sense to me, in some way, that the younger brother should now try and pick up where JFK had been forced to leave off. I don't know what Andy and Tom and Karen felt. But the next morning we slept with our pillows crushed up against the car doors as Dad drove straight to Indianapolis on the I-65. Dad and Mom got connected with the Kennedy campaign and we went from door to door while Mom phoned homes from the campaign office.

It wasn't a hard thing. All of us were busy and I realize now the campaign kept us from brooding over Uncle M.L. and just moping and grieving around our house back in Canada. It made a difference for us to fight back. And it was fun. There were rallies with streamers and balloons and free food and cake. That whole month until the Indiana primary still seems like a rush of colour to me, like one huge painting. I read the books now and I know how tough the campaign was. But it was something I believed Uncle M.L. would be proud of and it was exhilarating to be caught up in the intensity. Suddenly I thought it was great to be out of school for this, summer school or no summer school.

No one spoke like Uncle M.L. But Bobby had his moments. Dad brought Andy and I along to a couple of speeches. Bobby got angry at a bunch of smug med students at the Indiana University Medical School: "I look around this room and I don't see many black faces who will become doctors. Part of civilized society is to let people go to medical school who come from ghettos. You don't see many people coming out of ghettos or off the Indian reservations to medical school. You are the privileged ones. It's our society, not just our government, that spends twice as much on pets as on the poverty program. It's the poor who carry the major burden in Vietnam. You sit here as white medical students, while black people carry the burden of the fighting in Vietnam."

He never had Uncle M.L.'s rolling eloquence and magnificent baritone. He joked more, he lost his temper, he grinned and made short quips. But as I listened to him on TV or at the rallies I enjoyed him. I liked him because he was young and got excited like a kid and said exactly what he felt. I wanted him to make people laugh or clap and when they did, it was like they were coming alongside our family and our family's friend and alongside a friend of Uncle M.L. and alongside the same beliefs that Uncle M.L. had believed. I sensed some sort of unbroken chain between Memphis and Indianapolis.

Bobby won Indiana with 42% and the District of Columbia too, with 62.5%. Dad pointed the car west for Nebraska, barreling along the I-74 to pick up the I-80 into Lincoln at Rock Island, Illinois. But not before taking us on a quick sidetrip to Springfield to visit Abraham Lincoln's grave. The grave was big, too big, a monument really. Yet the grave of the assassinated president who freed the slaves made us think about Uncle M.L.'s grave in Atlanta. The rest of the trip into Nebraska we were all moody and irritable.

Nebraska only lasted a week for us. We drove from place to place and cheered at the rallies and Mom phoned people and Karen and Andy and Tom and I ran from house to house with grins and pamphlets. Bobby's last speech was in Omahain a rain storm. It was the black part of town and I felt more comfortable there, as if I was at Mason Temple with Uncle M.L. and the shouting congregation. Bobby was trying to talk outdoors in the storm, all of us getting soaked, and he asked us, "Have any of you noticed that it's raining?"

"Yes!" we yelled.

"If there are silly things to do then this is the silliest. It's silly for you to be standing in the rain listening to a politician. As George Bernard Shaw once said, 'Run for the buses!'"

That was his standard line, always quoting George Bernard Shaw, especially the phrase, 'Some men see things as they are and ask why. I dream things that never were and ask why not?' Shaw never told anyone to run for the buses. Knowing what I know about Shaw now though, I think the old Irishman would have liked it.

We won on May 14th with 51.5%. We couldn't lose. We fuelled up the wagon and headed for Oregon and the coast, staying on the I-80 until we hit Utah and then taking the I-84 right into Portland. There was a Democratic primary in South Dakota, so close to home Mom wondered why we couldn't head north instead of west.

"You know, Mother," Dad said. "Oregon and California are going to tell the tale."

But we lost in Oregon. We had been going all out for weeks with the Kennedy campaign and when Eugene McCarthy edged Bobby 44.7% to 38.8% Mom and Dad had a big fight. She wanted to go home. He told her to go home but he was staying. In the end, they went outside the motel room and worked it through and kissed. They agreed they would spend one more week campaigning for Bobby and then head back to Canada. We had done our part, Dad said. "We'll win in South Dakota and we'll win in California," Dad promised. "Bobby and M.L. will get back on track. Bobby will get the nod at the Convention in Chicago. He'll be the Democratic candidate for the election this fall. And the American people will make him president."

We went door to door and phoned and rallied and cheered in Sacramento and Fresno and Bakersfield. Dad had a friend who was a pastor in Oakland and we finally met Bobby there. He shook our hands and smiled and said he couldn't believe we had been campaigning in Indiana, Nebraska, and Oregon before showing up in California.

"Are you in it for the money?" he asked me.

I shrugged. "We do it for Uncle M.L."

My Dad explained, "John was close to M.L., to Martin Luther King. He was a family friend."

Bobby sobered up instantly and put a hand on my shoulder: "Then it's a great thing to have you on my side."

He went on into West Oakland for a ghetto rally and we followed him there. Mom kept us close, she was frightened by the Black Panthers who were shouting, "Free Huey!" But no one touched us. By the time Bobby had finished speaking, the Black Panthers were clearing the path for his car so it could get through the crowd. It was hard not to think of all the African Americans who swarmed around Uncle M.L.

"I guess they believe him," Dad said as we got back to our station wagon.

"I believe him," Mom responded. "Coretta believes him."

"So you think the last two months was worth it?"

"Yes, it was worth it. But after this primary I want to go home."

"On Wednesday morning we are scooting up the I-5 to Vancouver and we are going home."

Mom smiled and rested one hand on Dad's knee while she leaned her head against the window.

We watched the returns on the TV in our motel room, but even with our excitement over Bobby winning in California and South Dakota, it got pretty boring.

"Why can't we go down to the Ambassador for the victory rally?" asked Andy.

It was about eleven and Dad shook his head. "It's too late. It'll be too crowded. We're on our way in the morning."

"But I'd really like to go to the rally, Dad."

"Why? To see more pretty American girls? Get some sleep, Andy. We're having breakfast at seven."

In LA we had rented two rooms side by side with a connecting door. Andy and I went through and lay down on the beds in our room. Tom and Karen were sleeping in Mom and Dad's room. I talked to God and I talked to Uncle M.L. before I fell asleep. "He'll be president now, Uncle M.L.," I whispered. "Everything is going to keep on. You can rest easy about that." Hope and joy can give you good sleep. Solid greens and blues swept through my dreams. I woke up feeling brand new.

Sunlight was pouring across my bed. Andy was already up and out. I couldn't hear anyone. It was so quiet I thought they'd all gone for breakfast without me. I didn't care. I stretched my legs and turned over my pillow to its cool side. I was in delicious peace. I just wanted to lie there and listen to the silence. Summer was coming, the sun was warm and golden, and the world was perfectly round.

As I lay looking at the bars of bright light on the wall Dad came into the room through the connecting door. He was as quiet as everything else.

"You up, John?" he asked softly.

"Where's everybody?" I asked.

"They're in the car. We thought we'd head along the I-5 for awhile and then pull over for breakfast."

"Okay."

"Are you hungry?"

"No."

"Well, get dressed, we're waiting for you."

Dad walked around the room and toyed with a book and a lamp and tugged at my jeans I'd tossed over a chair. He had never come into the room before and I couldn't understand what he was doing, wandering around with an empty look to his face and fiddling with things. He stopped by the window and looked out, playing with the cord for the venetian blinds. Finally, he said, "Bobby was shot last night at the Ambassador."

The blur of balloons and faces and all the colours that had taken me down into sleep stopped. I have read a dozen books about those two months between April 4th and June 4th but I gave up on them a long time ago. They always end the same way. Everyone dies. It took me thirty years to realize I end with them and begin with them. Thirty years to open the doors a bit and look at the balcony of the Lorraine and the ballroom of the Ambassador with its one red rose, to see everything in a clear morning light: Why I never fit in with the white middle class churches. Why I never fit in with the students at seminary who would never rock a boat to save their souls. Why I was always arguing with some professor in law school who loved to quote Oliver Wendell Holmes, "Do not speak to me of justice, young man. This is a court of law." I never stopped being angry my whole life and I never came home after that June morning in California.

We drove all day on June 5th. We needed to get away from LA in the same way we had needed to get away from Memphis. Mom kept the radio on. Bobby was still alive. By the time we pulled up to a motel in southern Oregon we felt a surge of courage because he was continuing to fight for his life.

"He'll pull through," Dad said.

We ate a bit and went to bed at midnight and Bobby was still doing well. I slept because I hoped and the hope gave me peace and coloured all my dreams in a final stain of innocence. No one turned on the TV or the car radio in the morning when we headed out again. I think Dad had the feeling we could keep death at bay and Bobby alive if we didn't allow dark thoughts or negative commentary to intrude. But we had to stop for gas and breakfast in Roseburg and the newspapers were black with headlines. For awhile Dad even pretended not to see them. Until Mom wept in the restaurant and he scooped up napkins for her eyes. But what settled into him from June 6th on was not grief but fury.

Dad never preached again. When I graduated from seminary with my Masters of Divinity he did not congratulate me and when I followed my Masters up with law school in the United States he made no comment. I went to Bobby Kennedy's alma mater at the University of Virginia but even that could not budge him. When I passed the Virginia bar and came back north for a visit I noticed he had left my room in the basement exactly the same. There was Uncle M.L.'s picture and there was Bobby's picture and there was a poster I had made myself, handprinting every word of Uncle M.L.'s I Have A Dream speech.

Mom grew tired and old very quickly through the '70's and '80's, smoking two packs of cigarettes a day, gaining an enormous amount of weight, filling herself with prescription pills as if she were swallowing peanuts. Dad lasted another ten years after her but having fought off cancer three times, finally succumbed. I put a cross of olive wood around his neck during his final days. I'd brought it home from Israel. He asked me to read to him from the Bible.

"I never told you something," he said one afternoon when we were sitting together at the end of a hospital corridor.

"What is it, Dad?"

"Bobby wanted to see you again. He actually called the motel. Or somebody did for him. Then he got on the line. You were out getting milk. He was feeling pretty good because the results were coming in from South Dakota and California and everything was coming up roses."

"What did he want?"

"He wanted you to walk his dog Freckles with him on Redondo Beach. He thought you'd like that. I forgot all about his call until the next morning. After that, I just didn't bother telling you. I didn't know what good it would do."

I hadn't cried about those crazy two months for years but I felt my face burning and my throat tightening. I got up and went to the toilet in Dad's room and came back. Dad watched me.

"You're keeping ahold of all the anger," he said.

"Just like you."

"I wonder if it didn't help kill me."

"Don't talk like that. You've beaten it before."

"How do you feel about the world, John?"

"What? A complacent church that stands up for nothing and cares more for its pretty little programs than for people?"

"What about the law?"

"Another loser. My friends couldn't wait to scoop up the jobs with the corporations. Who wants to be a public defender of the poor and the oppressed? The students who grew up in the '60's are the biggest sellouts the earth has ever seen."

"Nothing is good."

"No. Nothing is good."

"The anger keeps you warm."

"The anger keeps me going."

"Where will you practice next?"

"California. There's a public interest firm. They work with the Hispanic community in San Diego."

"So you can be angry for all of them too."

"I guess."

"I don't think I did such a good thing, Johnny. I shut down after Los Angeles. Your mother and I both closed up shop. We put everything into keeping M.L. alive. We were sure we could do it through Bobby. His assassination meant M.L.'s mortality was unavoidable. The whole house of cards came down. It wasn't just that M.L. died twice. Bobby died too. Your mother and I had grown to like him. Tell me, John King, would you call Bobby Kennedy a spiteful, ruthless man?"

"No."

"What about M.L.? Was he full of rage?"

"No."

"So where did you get yours from if your heroes didn't have any?"

"Their killers gave it to me. And a lot of flaky churches that didn't care about anything more than a body count and twelve noon so they could go home. And a lot of law students who think justice is a Disneyland fantasy for the naive."

"I'm just wondering how M.L. would want you to live."

"Look, Dad, you're pretty good at thriving on the old anger yourself."

"It wasn't a good idea. It ate your mother and I up from the inside out. But Karen and Andy and Tom are free from it. I don't want it to fuel the next forty years of your life."

"What is going to fuel it?"

"What fuelled M.L.?"

"Who knows?"

"But you do know. Love. His faith in God. His faith in people."

"Come on, Dad. Let's forget this."

"Bobby changed after his brother's death. Love poked through the pain and the toughness."

"Well, I can't be like them."

"Can you be like Jesus?"

"What? Are you going to go back to preaching?"

Dad lifted himself up in bed and thrust his face at mine. Everything came out of his eyes and out of his words.

"John King. M.L. and Bobby made the world rich. One was black, one was white, one was a Baptist, the other was a Catholic, and they made the world a splendid place for a season. That is why we love them so much. They were not furies. They were lovers. They made a greatness. It's still not gone. It lingers. I think it was meant to linger in you.

"I know very well how weak churches can be. But you don't have to sway all of them. You just need to win over a few to start. Jesus hardly had anybody. All through history you have Christians jumping to the side of the powerbrokers. A handful don't. These are the ones who love change into being and they can't be beaten down. You can rail about the softness of the German Christians during the Third Reich. But you can't dismiss the Swiss theologian Barth or the German pastors Niemoller and Bonhoeffer. You can't ignore those who took the Jews into their homes and hid them. You can't pretend there were none who defied Hitler in the peace of God and paid for it with their lives. Have Christians been slave owners? Other Christians confronted them to their face and told them they were wrong. It was Wilberforce and the Christians who led the fight against slavery in Britain. It was the Christian abolitionists and the Quakers who led the fight against slavery in the States. You make up your mind, John King, who you are.

"M.L. wanted to restore the beloved community. Bobby wanted to make gentle the world. Lincoln appealed to the better angels of our nature. They were fighters but they enriched us. I want you to go on and take a piece of the world and breathe on it until it blossoms with flowers. Fight your foes relentlessly and love your foes relentlessly. Until they can't fight you anymore because they are overpowered by grace. Make God's Kingdom come. The wolf with the lamb. The leopard with the goat. The calf and the lion at peace. A little child leading them.

"You were the little child, John King. Take your innocence back. Go on. It's God's gift. It isn't lost once and forever. I thought that was so but I was wrong. Before I die I want to hear that you are going to be known neither for harming nor destroying on all God's holy mountain. Mould the complacent and the cruel back into the image of God. You come back to life and you do this, John King. I know you left a boy in Memphis and LA. Get him back. You don't let anyone steal the child. The killers didn't kill M.L. and Bobby and you just make up your mind they are not going to kill you. Thy Kingdom come. You go that way, John King. Don't let anybody turn you around."

I listened to him and I said, "You are sounding more like Uncle M.L. everyday."

Dad sank back in his chair. "Help me back to my room, John. I need to lie down."

I got him into bed and the nurse checked on him and I turned down the lamp. He smiled in the yellow glow.

"That felt good," he said faintly.

I smiled too. "Tearing a strip off your son?"

"I wasn't tearing a strip off. I was trying to put one back on. Come by tomorrow. We'll talk some more. I guess I'm played out now."

I was hanging on to his thin hand. "Okay, Dad."

"You tell John King it's a good night. I forgot to relay that to you, too. Tell John King good night from me. I'll see him down on the beach." Dad squeezed my hand as much as he could, a far cry from the days when I was a boy and he used to be able to crush my fingers in his grip. "Good night, John King."

"Good night, Dad."

And that was it. I went out for a burger before heading back to our old house and the hospital called a moment after I came through the door. I phoned my brothers and my sister and then I went out and sat on the front steps, the same place I'd sat for forty years whenever I was home and the weather was warm. It was May and my birthday was coming up. There were long green fields across the street. They would never build on them because the airport was just there. Green and gold got together, burned a minute, and then the sky was a purple dark jangling with bells like the mules' harness.

I went back to Memphis and the Lorraine Motel and I left a red rose there and another at Uncle M.L.'s grave in Atlanta. I went to Arlington and left a third rose at Bobby's small white cross. Then it was time to drive to the coast. I followed the same route our family had taken across the country in 1968. When I got to LA I stopped at the Ambassador Hotel and left a fourth rose on the kitchen floor when there were no staff nearby.

I slept at the hotel and woke early. It was an LA day without mist or fog and the sun rose slowly behind me as I walked along Redondo Beach. I took off my shoes and stepped into the Pacific. The cold water burned against my legs. I waited until the light of the low slanting rays had fastened itself over me like a new skin of bright gold. I took a final red rose from a sheet of green paper and I flung the rose into the sea.

"Good night, John King," I said.

Then I climbed back up to my car and started the drive south to San Diego and the public interest firm there and the small church that met in an old Spanish chapel that needed a preacher. I thanked God that the traffic was sparse and that the sun was strong on this first day of creation when I intended to work alongside him to love and to be fruitful and to replenish the earth.

CHAPTER 14

THE BOOK OF WONDERS

He kept two journals. One he called the Book of Wounds, the other the Book of Wonders. He began the first after he had been a pastor for two years. He started the second with the hope it would have an ameliorating effect on the first. He needed an antidote for the poison. Maybe it was not such a good idea to keep the Book of Wounds but he could not help himself. Everytime a Christian in one of his congregations slapped him on the back with one hand and slipped the long knife into his back with the other he had to go somewhere with his pain and grief. It was not enough to unburden himself with his wife or his friends. It was not enough to be prayed over, not even enough for him to pray on his own. He had to write. Of course, what he wrote were his real prayers but he did not realize that for a long time. Then he understood why the psalms had come to be written down. There was something about pen and mind and language and despair coming together on a sheet of paper. It fuelled his outrage but it also gave the outrage a safe place to go.

He often returned to the Book of Wounds even when he was not wounded. There was a kind of tragic poignancy in his written cries. They stirred him. He had a sense that one day there would be a vindication. That God had heard the years of words, sentence after sentence, page after page. In fact, they became a kind of daily bread that he returned to regularly to feed his anguish.

He became very good at anticipating the knife thrusts of congregations and staff and best friends who only wanted the best for him, the best for the church and the best for God, but who mostly wanted the best for themselves. No sooner had he anticipated the attacks then they came, singly or in clusters. Immediately he would go to the Book. It was satisfying to add more ink to the journal. In ten years it became a weighty tome. There was always fresh material, church after church, ministry after ministry. On quiet nights while his wife and his children slept he would dip into the pages once again and remember. The hot flame of betrayal never went out.

His sermons became brittle and flinty, his public prayers sharp. He ignored the concerns of those, even his wife, who asked him about this. Yet alone in his study he knew something was petrifying him. The Book of Wounds could not take the edge from his heart. No doubt the Book whetted it. That was when he decided on the Book of Wonders as an attempt at an antivenin. A kind of count-your-blessings journal to balance the other.

For the first few years the Book of Wonders came along very slowly, there were probably three or four entries in the Book of Wounds to every one in the Book of Wonders. It seemed he could only walk the stony road of Christian ministry as a via dolorosa, never as a via dolce. The latter seemed a frivolity, a trivializing of the harsh reality of Gesthemane and Golgotha. It came too close to the slapstick holler-hallelujah Christian sit-com that went for religious broadcasting for most of the TV evangelists. Put on the garment of praise for the spirit of heaviness, just slap it on like a toothy smile, and everything would be okay.

Yet he grew to wonder at the Book of Wonders. He found himself returning to it almost as frequently as he did to the Book of Wounds. He pondered one night that God's first words in the Bible should be the fiat lux. Closely on these thoughts came an image of children crawling into Jesus' lap and wanting a story, a hug and a tussle. He saw the garden at the end of the world with its crystal river and its orchard of fruit that could heal the earth, with its splendid light that needed no sun just as the fiat lux needed no sun. Suddenly he could not stop writing in the Book of Wonders. Brightness gushed out of some kind of cracked shell inside.

He attempted to regulate the flood for a time by insisting he keep a balance, that for every entry of wonder there must be another in the other journal of a wounding. But in the end he could not keep this balance. He was inundated with light. Gratitude broke out of his pen every morning and every night. In one year the Book of Wonders filled as many pages as the Book of Wounds had in ten. His sermons resonated like arias from the bella vita of an Italian tenor. He prayed and he slept in his prayers and he woke and he was a man alive.

But the Book of Wonders could not stop the nails. It might try and make sense of them. It might even try to be thankful for them. Yet they drove through skin and bone and spirit just the same. In his fifteenth year of pastoral ministry, in his favourite church, through his favourite friend, at his brightest moment, the knife of betrayal went in, and the nails of betrayal went in, and the weight of the pain pinned him to the earth so that he could not move. No matter what he wrote he could not breathe. He could only die.

It was impossible to go to the Book of Wonders. Its fire was too boisterous for his night. He had ignored the Book of Wounds for almost two years. He thought this had meant a healing. But now as the pain came on and on and fastened into him with teeth as cruel and long as winter he turned its pages once more. At first he could not even find it. It was under a stack of old magazines. He was afraid to open it, recalling his savage delight at self-flagellation that had kept the ache and the fury throbbing in the old days. But in desperation he sat alone again in his study and wondered, not for the first time since he had become a pastor, if indeed there was a God whom his life and death mattered to, and he opened the Book.

How strange a night it was. It seemed to go on forever. He had forgotten there would be an eclipse so that he was startled to step out into the yard for air and see the earth's shadow blotting out the moon. The moon became the colour of blood and he could see that it was not a silver disc but in fact a sphere, it took on its true shape and substance in the dark of the shadow of the world. The night was as clear as fresh water and the stars were even more luminous in the haunting subjugation of the moon, the lesser light to rule the night no longer able to do so with the brash splendour of the sun. Yet in its abjection it continued to command attention and to give an eerie mystery and a grandeur to the sky that was never there when the light reflected off its surface unhindered. The moon seemed more vital now. It seemed more real. He saw that under this dark and ruddy moon the universe was indeed a place of shapes hidden and distances unknown and truths unrealized until the long shadows should come and, in obscurity, make all things clear.

He returned to the Book of Wounds and finished it by four in the morning. The moon was bright silver again and low in the sky and the great revelation was lost to the human eye. He wrote down in a new passage what he had seen and felt and known. The pain he had carried ran swiftly from his body and his spirit into the pen and into the language of the Book. Then he closed the Book. He went back outside to face the east. He was filled with peace.

Slowly the great star rose with reds more lustrous, with a light more frightening and wondrous. As it came it gave depth and dimension to all his features and sculpted them in the purest gold of the dawn of the earth. He smiled as the night gave way to all the colours and the movements of the air and the warming of the grass and the trees and the land. Then he turned aside. There was much to do. There was much to desire and to relish, much to pray and much to live over a second time since the Book of Wounds itself had become the Book of Wonders.

CHAPTER 15

SNOW ANGELS

His were always bigger. He was two years older, fifteen pounds heavier, more than a foot taller. So he developed a broader wingspan and train and he had a way of twisting his neck from side to side to give himself a full head of curls. But his sister was clean and tight and had strength in her legs from ballet classes, so when she rose up she needed no one's help, nor did she ever put a boot in the wrong place. There was always a boot print or two under his angel but hers looked as if someone had dropped out of the sky, landed, lay down, and left with the beauty of wings.

They grew up and went their own ways. When the families gathered at Mom and Dad's for Christmas each year the brother and sister made the snow angels, their children made the snow angels, and eventually their children's children made the snow angels. Once the brother told his sister bitterly, "The only angels God ever sent to watch over our lives are these and they melt with the sun." Yet he flung himself down with his sons and daughters and alongside his sister and her sons and daughters, just as their own father and mother had flung themselves down beside the two of them and fanned their arms and legs and tried to rise without marking the angels' trains with boot prints. There, under the bare cottonwoods, under a golden lamp in the park, under the silver slivers of the stars, one generation had lain, and another, and another, every Christmas, and every year there were angels, large and small, one, two, three, a multitude of the heavenly host, fresh at creation, some with swords in their hands, some with doves, gleaming by night, flashing like lightning in the sun of the day, shrinking into themselves as they aged and as the season warmed, yet the snow that remained the longest when all else but the mounds left by the plows had melted, clinging to themselves and their swords until the sun grew so large and brilliant nothing could stand.

The months brought the mother and the father and the brother and the sister and all the children and the children's children cruelty and despair and darkness. The years brought them disappointment and decay and death. But in the snow by the creek, with the truth of mountains on the black wind, they lay in their laughter while a thousand lights blazed on houses and drainpipes and evergreens and rooftops. The never-to-be-seen-again snowflakes formed droplets on their sons' fat happy cheeks and upon their daughters' bright teeth and loose hair, and where angels were birthed no hatred came, no spite, no sin or wickedness, no scorching tongues. A young woman's love spread its wings there and newborn fatherhood and motherhood too, and sisterhood and brotherhood, cousins fell there together and rose, wet with white, cold up their legs and arms and down their necks, and there under old cottonwoods that creaked like gates and doors opening they grew and knew and carried the secrets of night angels into the day or the shining charm of a morning angel into the dusk. They came again and again and the angels came to them under the perpetual skies that gave them the light and the air and the glittering ice and crystal, the stuff of angels' hair and angel wings.

So the brother and sister stood together with a dozen grandchildren and three great-grandchildren, he was eighty-nine and she was eighty-seven, and he leaned on a sturdy blackthorn cane, and the angels leaped out of the snow as they had done for a hundred years. The children laughed and shouted and shivered and made another and another and another. He could feel the aches of heart and body and spirit melt and slough off him only then, only there, in all his years of prayer and faith and faltering steps, and he said to his sister, "You cannot come here and make angels in the summer. I wish you could."

She gave his arm, still strong and sinewy, a hard squeeze. "The winter is right. In the winter we need them."

A boy called and wondered if the blackthorn cane would not make a fine sword. Before his sister could talk him out of it, the man seized her hand and pulled her down into the tabula rasa with him and they thrashed their arms and legs and snow flew into their ears and noses and they laughed together again like a ringing. He flung out his cane and it instantly became the sword, perhaps the one that had flashed at Eden and that would flash again in peace when all things in heaven and earth came together in the Christ of Christmas, and he pressed himself deeper and deeper into the angel that was himself. The once-in-a-lifetime snowflakes came into his skin and into him and all of it had come together and was of one piece and all of it was good and it was all of it creation and the morning stars sang together for joy and the angels were the winds and they were the bright fire in the winter's night.

CHAPTER 16

TOMORROW SHALL BE MY DANCING DAY

She had plucked cards from plastic loaves of bread. Risen at four or five or six to kneel. Gone through every new translation, gone back to the King James Version, taken courses in Greek and Hebrew and tried to read the Bible in its original tongues. She had tried Robert Murray Mc'Cheyne's daily reading plan and gone through the entire Bible once and the New Testament twice in a year. She had underlined in different colours. Taped verses on her fridge. Read one verse at a time, one chapter at a time, a whole book at a time.

Sometimes there was a gust of sparks in her soul. Sometimes a translation brought a verse home and there was a quick spurt of flame. She had cried when she read Luke's account of the crucifixion in Greek for the first time, all the nuances, all the inflections, all the subtleties, all the dying driven into her like long sharp iron. Once, by her bed, at four in the morning, it was as if an angel had passed and lightly brushed her fair hair with a hand. A number of times she was sure God was listening when she prayed, she heard him listening, and once or twice she knew she was listening to him, not just waiting to recite her shopping list of needs and requests. Once she slept praying and dreamed a golden dream of Jesus in the wilderness. His temptations were over and she was offering him fresh fruit she had split open with a silver knife.

But mostly her knees grew sore and cracked painfully when she rose. Often the Bible was like a dead stick in her hands and said nothing, gave nothing, grew nothing. She came to resent the cards from the loaf of bread. They were always positive, always upbeat, as if they were part of a Christian Zodiac that she came to daily for her horoscope. Where were the verses that cried her pain, her depression, her despair? She knew they were in the Bible somewhere but they were never in the plastic loaf of bread. Nor were they ever on her fridge. Am I trying to brainwash myself? she thought one morning and tore the verses from the white fridge door. God, please, my God, I don't want positive thinking, I want faith, I want to see all the black and white and grey and I want to see you right in the middle of it all.

For years she felt guilty whenever she missed her quiet time, her time alone with God in prayer and Bible reading. If something bad happened to her that day she was certain God was punishing her for not praying or reading her Bible. Sometimes she would get angry at the ritual she felt she must perform in order to appease her God and rebel in a frustrated fury, as if she had to escape from bars and locks and drudgery God had imposed on her, her church had imposed on her, she had imposed on herself hoping God would be pleased with her efforts and reward her in tangible ways. So often the rewards did not come, at least not any rewards she expected or recognized, and she saw people who did not pray or read their Bibles or even believe in God doing as well or better than she did in all aspects of their lives. She would turn away from her quiet time for weeks and months in her bitterness. It solved nothing for she felt dirty and unclean in her rebellion, nor did the righteous anger she felt at the pointless imprisonment of her morning devotions dispel any of her guilt. When she returned to the quiet time, weeping in repentance, she was refreshed and renewed, as if bright white snow had blanketed her inner being and her mind calmed under a sky of a million winking lights. But then life caught up with her again, her knees ached, the Bible was dead and silent, prayers were not answered, the opposite of what she pleaded for occurred again and again, and she felt trapped in saying certain prayers in certain ways with certain endings and beginnings and expressions and turns of phrase. She wondered if the relief she felt when she returned to her quiet times, after spells of honest rejection of what stultified her, was not merely the relieved settlement of the mind into the barn and stable and manger it knew, the relief of the return to the security of routine, the peace of what was commonplace, the contentment afforded by the rutted tracks that always led in the same direction in the same way, bypassing the forests and the mountains and the long unknown meadows of orange poppies and purple thistles. Perhaps it was the neurotic's joy at returning to the neurosis, the comfort of the habit, the pleasure of an essential addiction.

She leaned over the island in the centre of the kitchen once, over pota-toes and carrots and celery and beets, and thought: What if God wants me to run through the orange poppies? The thought brought immediate exhil-aration, for an hour she felt like a young burning Christian again, ready to take on the world, filled with all the light and crystal of heaven. Then old thoughts came and tugged her back down to earth. Quiet time was what quiet time was. Experimentation was dangerous.

But what if, she thought again, at Halloween with the windows of the neighbourhood yellow and orange with jack o' lanterns and the night com-ing on quickly, what if God doesn't care if I'm on my knees or not, does-n't care what time of the day I pray or what words I use or don't use? What if there's no formula? No manual? No ritual? Nothing necessary but to run to him? Through the long fields of purple thistles and orange poppies? What if we run and run and make our own path to God in prayer? What if it is only necessary to be through the gate and into Christ's acres and roam there in worship and discovery? What if we are free to sit under the oak or under the willow, to go down by the cataract or the hissing whitewater or the millpond the colour of molasses? What if we are at liberty to pur-sue God? And if it rains in Christ's meadows, if it storms, that's all right, isn't it, because they're his meadows?

These thoughts poured in so that light and air streamed through her soul and this was followed by a great wind that howled and scoured and plucked much free to roll in a morning of all her being. She could not sit still. She could not sleep. She moved in and out of the rooms of her small house, thinking and feeling and praying fiercely. The sun rose outside her home, a rain had crystallized to a light snow during the night, and Halloween had become All Saints Day. She put her two German Shepherds into her van and drove out of the city to an open field without trees that bordered a lake. The snowy field glistened in the sun, long and white and clean, and the dogs raced in strong joy over its unblemished sur-face, hunting mice, flinging themselves on their backs and wriggling in its coolness, thrusting their noses under it and rolling and barking and yip-ping and wrestling each other and running again. She was alone in all the blue sky and white miles and she threw up her arms and began to sing as she had not sung for years, right from her stomach and throat, as loudly and for as long as she could expel her breath, hymns, carols, melodies she filled with her own words, arias as great and expansive as all the spa-ciousness she whirled within. Her spirit was brighter than the bright burning land of the million gleamings she rang in and sang in. My God, how she prayed, how she played, how she worshipped. My God, how she loved.

Printed in the United States
6698

9 781573 832052